THE BEAUTY MAKERS

Everyone knows the great cosmetic house of Vermeyer; many women know the elegant façade of the Vermeyer building in New York. But not even the more fashionable among them, who have experienced the luxury of the Vermeyer showrooms, have any knowledge of the ruthless struggle for success fought out beyond the gracious salons on the ground floor. This novel takes you into that world—a world in which the weaknesses and the foibles of womankind are studied, analysed and exploited, a highly competitive world in which a mistake can spell disaster or a bright new idea make a fortune.

It is the story of the people who matter in Vermeyers—of Paul Vandenberg who controls the whole organization, austere, unapproachable, but when you get to know him, a very human person acutely aware of his failure to achieve any real happiness; a man whose future is shadowed by the constant threat of angina. Paul Vandenberg's life had been a succession of triumphs; his success with each enterprise he took over was inevitable, and The House of Vermeyer was no exception. For Harry Sarnoff, who first knew Vermeyers as a bath-tub business in a back-street room, and for Gloria Vernon, the original 'Vermeyer Girl', he was a necessary evil. For Sigrid Anderson, Sarnoff's young, idealistic secretary, he became the centre of existence. It is their love affair with its tenderness and its passionate intensity, haunted by the knowledge that time is running out too fast, upon which this novel turns.

But it is, above all, the story of The House of Vermeyer, told with an intimate knowledge of the beauty business; a story which will intrigue every woman who finds herself expensively susceptible to the luscious presentation of each new cosmetic launched in a fragrant cloud of petal-dust.

THE
BEAUTY MAKERS

by
N. B. LAMONT

CASSELL · LONDON

CASSELL & COMPANY LTD
35, Red Lion Square
London, W.C.1
and at

210 Queen Street, Melbourne; 26/30 Clarence Street, Sydney; 24 Wyndham Street, Auckland; 1068 Broadview Avenue, Toronto 6; P.O. Box 275, Cape Town; P.O. Box 11190, Johannesburg; Haroon Chambers, South Napier Road, Karachi; 13/14 Ajmeri Gate, Extension, New Delhi 1; 15 Graham Road, Ballard Estate, Bombay 1; 17 Chittaranjan Avenue, Calcutta 13; P.O. Box 23, Colombo; Macdonald House, Orchard Road, Singapore 9; Avenida 9 de Julho 1138 São Paulo; Galeria Güemes, Escritorio 454/59 Florida 165, Buenos Aires; Marne 5b, Mexico 5, D.F.; Sanshin Building, 6 Kanda Mitoschiro-cho, Chiyoda-ku, Tokyo; 25 rue Henri Barbusse, Paris 5e; 25 Ny Strandvej, Espergaerde, Copenhagen; Beulingstraat 2, Amsterdam-C; Bederstrasse 51, Zürich 2

Set in 12 pt. Bembo type and Printed in Great Britain by
Butler & Tanner Ltd, Frome and London
358

I

PAUL VANDENBERG watched the progress of the test silently, a slight, austere, not over-tall man, with a face not easily forgotten. It would have been handsome, but for something in it that spoke of sickness. But it was not that which stayed in the mind. It was a quality in the expression that was hard to define. At one moment he looked at you, and there was nothing in his eyes, you didn't exist; and then it was there, an all-knowing, encompassing, deadly discernment that ripped into you and revealed even your thoughts, or so it seemed.

An adversary had dubbed him bitterly, in a moment of defeat: 'the poker player with the crystal ball'. On being told of the sobriquet, Vandenberg had simply smiled. He knew you didn't need a crystal ball. All you needed was to know a man's breaking point. If you knew that, and could wait, inevitably you got what you wanted.

Louis Vermeyer had reached his breaking point, and now The House of Vermeyer was just one more Vandenberg venture. And as Paul Vandenberg watched the procedures set up by his predecessor, it was hard to say whether the victory had afforded him any satisfaction.

The doctors were testing the newest basecoat to be used under nail enamel. The patch test was part of the regular ritual of the company. Every new product, every new batch of an old product, had to be tested before it was placed on the market. The House of Vermeyer, the colossus of the beauty business, took no chances. There had been a time when it was different. Sure, then it had been easy. You mixed up a bottle and that was all there was to it. What if something went wrong occasionally? What if a few women lost a finger-nail or two? In the early days, you shrugged it off. But now beauty was a multi-million dollar business, and the company presided over by this slim, dark-haired man was the biggest of the lot. It couldn't afford to take chances.

In groups of ten at a time, the girls filed before the doctors, their backs bared to receive the patches. Some of them stood nonchalantly enough in their slips, others clutched blouses about them self-consciously. There were plump girls, slim girls, blondes, brunettes, redheads and plain but well-groomed mouse. About them all was a certain stamp of similarity—a sort of spurious, mass-produced beauty. Most of them disliked being 'on test', but they knew better than to complain. If you complained, you were labelled unco-operative. There could be no more damning verdict in a company where every female employee was a stand-in for the feminine public.

The ritual followed an unchanging pattern. A small dab of liquid or a smear of cream was applied to the upper back, and covered by an adhesive pad. When each girl had received her first patch the line filed before the doctors again, and a second and a third up to eight patches were applied. The Interview Room, where the tests were held, resembled nothing so much at these moments as a first-aid station. The doctors in their white coats worked around a display table, on which were arranged in neat rows test bottles, gauze and adhesive tape, big wads of cotton-wool, and a bottle of purplish, antiseptic fluid. The clinical atmosphere contrasted bizarrely with the lush, off-white carpet and the dawn-pink walls.

To one of the girls at least, Sigrid Anderson, secretary to the Vice-President, the scene had a ludicrously unreal aspect. Three men of medicine wasting their fine brains and their deep concentration on one-eighth of an ounce of nail enamel. To irritate or not to irritate, that was the great scientific problem which confronted them. But she kept her thoughts to herself. If you wanted to succeed at Vermeyers you did not ridicule the testing procedures. And Ziggie Anderson wanted very much to succeed.

She was giving her personal particulars to Dr. Van Osten, youngest of the dermatological group. Name: Sigrid Anderson. Age: twenty-six. Complexion: fair. Always the same answers, always taken afresh at every test. She stood very straight, her face devoid of humour, like a good soldier. And then, because (like every other woman in the room) she was intensely aware of the presence of Vandenberg, she glanced across at him, obliquely. He was not looking at her, and she was glad; she felt at a disadvantage in her underwear. Sometimes her own boss, Harry Sarnoff, dropped in at the tests, and then the girls complained. She had reported it to him, and his reply had been typical. 'I've seen better on a beach.' But they didn't complain about the visits of the new President. No. Instead they preened themselves nervously like so many fluttering birds in a cage, their hands touching their hair to make sure no stray wisp marred their coiffure, their backs straightening in an unconscious gesture, the gesture of a woman the world over when an attractive man enters her orbit.

The doctors also reacted noticeably to Vandenberg's presence, as though, beneath that sardonic gaze, each man felt constrained to do his best. The good-humoured badinage ceased. Even O'Malley, the Chief Dermatological Consultant, stopped caressing the bare arms of the prettiest girls. (The discrimination was unintentional, his inherent good judgment in the matter of women betraying him. To a dermatologist of O'Malley's eminence and ambitions, every woman was but a step on the ladder. He wooed them only for their patronage and he loved them only for what they had already enabled him to achieve.)

Vandenberg addressed his remarks to O'Malley.

'How are the results shaping, so far?'

'Good. Ran it on two hundred girls at the plant last week, with completely negative results save for one girl, a reactor.'

'Sure she's a reactor?'

'Yes. We checked her record. Allergic to every nail enamel and basecoat that has ever been put on her.'

'Then keep her as a control. She shouldn't be run on routine test.'

Dr. James O'Malley, full professor in dermatology and syphilology, one of the five top names in the country in his field, paused. It still annoyed him that Vandenberg did not hesitate to tell him how to do his job. It annoyed him because he knew it was not the result of lack of tact. It was

Vandenberg's way of showing his contempt for a doctor who was willing to do this work.

O'Malley was a short, stocky, handsome man with alert blue eyes and the fresh blond complexion of a farmer. He coloured easily, and he coloured now. He knew Vandenberg noticed it, and that heightened his annoyance. To hell with his superiority, he thought. I've got the best clinic in New York. I do more good with the money I take from him than he would.

'How many tests are you running?' Vandenberg asked.

'Three hundred girls in all.'

'Not enough. I want at least five hundred.'

'Three hundred is more than the accepted safe minimum.'

'This is a basecoat. I want to be sure. Give me five hundred or more.'

O'Malley shrugged. 'Okay. It's your money.'

The girl before the doctors had a blemished back. Vandenberg stayed them as they were about to gesture to the next girl.

'Bad acne condition.'

'Yes. But it won't interfere with the test.'

'But something could be done about it?'

'Sure. If she wants to take some treatment.'

Vandenberg turned the girl around, examining her face as though it were a completely impersonal object. She was a very pretty girl in spite of the acne.

'What about the old scars?'

'They can be removed. Abrasion treatment.'

Vandenberg noticed the tension of the girl's clasped hands and the embarrassed flush in her cheeks. He spoke to her directly for the first time.

'You're Miss Rogers, aren't you?'

(His fantastic knack for getting to know the names of all his employees had become a by-word at Vermeyers.)

'Yes, sir.'

'You should have something done about that skin. You're a good-looking girl.'

'I couldn't—I don't want to.'

'Why? It would improve your looks.'

'It would mean—doctors' bills. I can't afford them.'

'It might not cost as much as you think. Let Dr. O'Malley take a look at it and map out a treatment. We'll see what it would cost. Doctor, send the bill for the first visit to the office.'

'Yes, sir.'

The girl moved on, thankful to be away from Vandenberg's scrutiny, and his impersonal glance continued to follow the test. And in spite of the lack of warmth, the unchanged demeanour of the man, O'Malley knew that the girl with acne would not be forgotten. A week or ten days from now he would receive a call from Vandenberg. A very nominal amount would be determined as the fee she should be charged, the rest would be paid by the company. If he commented on the President's generosity, he would be met with a cold: 'The faces of our girls are our shop-window. We can't afford blemished skins.' And even O'Malley would not know how far that covered it.

Things are different, he thought. It's less than a year, but things are very different. Vermeyer wouldn't have given a red cent for a girl's skin condition.

Satisfied that the test on the new basecoat was being accorded due importance, Vandenberg left as unobtrusively as he had come. He walked through the reception room and paused for a moment before the big display, recessed like a stage setting in a curtained alcove. It showed a willowy brunette mannequin (astonishingly lifelike) reclining in a hammock against a background of clematis sprays. Her organdie gown, palely yellow against the lilac of the walls, seemed to bring the spring sunshine into the room.

After perhaps a full minute's study, he walked over to the receptionist.

'Miss Adams. Will you please call Mr. Hirschberg.'

'I'm sorry, sir, Mr. Hirschberg is out. Won't be back till after lunch.'

'Then please take a message for him. That display needs changing. It composes badly. Tell him to shift the hammock one foot to the right. And the "Young Man's Fancy" sign should be out to the left, beyond the body of the group. The hat can be on the ground, beneath the mannequin's hand, as though she had dropped it. Got it?'

'Yes, sir.'

The receptionist was scribbling in fast longhand. She was a very attractive, superbly groomed young woman.

'Miss Adams, are you using "Young Man's Fancy"?'

She looked up, her brilliant smile faltering.

'No, sir. "So Red the Rose." It's my favourite.'

'I appreciate your choice for private wear, Miss Adams. But when you are on duty you are part of the display. I should consider it a personal favour if you would always wear the current promotion.'

Although couched in courteous terms, it was, she knew, an order. She was a little flustered.

'Why, of course, Mr. Vandenberg. I hadn't realized . . . .'

'There's no reason why you should, unless someone had told you. No harm done.'

And he smiled at her, gently, a smile that wiped out the coldness of his eyes and made her feel like singing. At that moment, for his smile she would have promised to wear 'Young Man's Fancy' for the rest of her life.

Vandenberg strolled back to his own office. It was a large, lavishly furnished room, yet with an austerity that pleased him. It was one of the few rooms that he had not altered.

He sat down in his deep couch, meditating. In this room he frequently thought of its former occupant: Louis Vermeyer— a man he could respect, a man as unswerving and as driving as Vandenberg himself, although he would not have put it that way. When the two met, it had been a meeting of equals. The son of Julian Vandenberg, who had made twenty million in the railroad business, had looked at Vermeyer, former Polish immigrant foundling who did not even know his true name, and recognized that fact.

Yet Vermeyer had failed. He had created a business, but he could not maintain it. In the early days of quick profits, it had mushroomed fantastically. He had climbed high and fast. But the greater his success, the more violently aggressive became the competition. Vermeyer knew both what women wanted and how to make them buy what he sold, but in the spiral of rising costs and tighter profit margins he had faced defeat.

[6]

Vandenberg had gone to work like a skilled surgeon, cutting away the sick growths that had flourished on Vermeyers. He closed plants, fired unnecessary staff, called to him the highly paid top executives who were in their present positions solely because they had been with Vermeyer from the beginning and told them they could go. He was not ungenerous. None of the persons let go could complain of the inadequacy of his severance pay. But overnight the personnel of the company was cut to half, and Vandenberg was not loved for it.

It was always the same story, he thought. You waited until you saw a company just ripe for this type of operation. Then you moved in. And after you had finished the job, you had a successful, healthy, corporate body, and it was your own achievement. Yet you were hated for it. People always overlooked the one significant fact—without this brutal surgery the company would have ceased to exist.

As Vandenberg sat in the elegant room where Louis Vermeyer had doubtless sat and exulted over early triumphs, he was thinking about the people now in his employ, and the people he had been forced to fire. What were they like? When you wiped away the assembly-line expressions painted on the girls' faces, when you overcame the deference or the hatred of the men, when you saw them in their own homes, apartments or furnished rooms—what were they? Were they the same flesh as he? Was there one among them with his own complex of desires, frustrations, and ambitions?

He was intensely aware of his isolation. It was more than loneliness. It had started by his being lonely. That had been easier. He had simply found someone to share a few hours with him. But this new isolation was different. It could not be overcome. If there were someone with him, it still existed. No one talked the same language that he did, no one seemed to know what was going on inside his mind. In recent years, only one man had seemed to get inside the shell. That was the man he had met scarcely a year ago, the man in whose room he now sat.

But it did him no good, that feeling of kinship with Louis Vermeyer. Because Louis, after making his deal with Vandenberg and providing for his family, had gone out quietly one night and thrown his body in front of a subway train at Times Square Station.

When you took a man's life-work away from him, there was nothing left. It didn't matter what you paid him for it. You took away his dreams. You took away a part of the man himself.

Yet he, Paul Vandenberg, still had his life-work. He had his empire. He was a legend, a myth, a man who at forty-four was reckoned among the giants. And it did no good. He sat in Vermeyer's room, and wondered what he had to live for that Vermeyer had not had, and he couldn't name it.

He was sick, he was tired, and he was intolerably alone.

II

HARRY SARNOFF lay in the tub, meditating. He frequently spent an hour in the tub. It was his one place of relaxation, the only retreat (although he wouldn't have used the word) left to modern man.

Sarnoff was not given to introspection, and therefore he never asked himself if he were happy. If someone else had asked him the question, he probably would have answered: 'You crazy? I got two Cadillacs, I got a twelve-room house in the best section of Westchester, my income tax is so high it would make your head spin...' And he would not have realized that he had not answered the question.

Sarnoff was undoubtedly successful. His one ambition as a young man had been to make money, and he had made it. But oddly enough it had not brought with it all that he had anticipated. It had not come early enough for him to take it for granted, and so he worried inordinately over the extravagances of his family. It brought him a host of so-called friends, but early in life he had lost the habit of trusting people, and so they remained on the fringe of his awareness. And his health was not good. (He was in fact as strong as an ox, but when you see men who have come up with you the hard way dying off in their forties from heart conditions you begin to worry, and when you begin to worry the body obediently complains.)

Perhaps, of all his disappointments, his family was the greatest. When the kids were young, they had been wonderful, but now they were growing up and growing away from him. They thought his accent was uncouth; they took what he gave them as their right; they were not willing to grant him the obedient adoration which he felt to be a father's due. Sarnoff had grown up in an atmosphere where papa was the boss; his children were growing up in the climate of freedom that was America.

It had been a rough year, Sarnoff thought, trying to pinpoint the vague dissatisfaction, almost depression, which habitually possessed him. With Vermeyer selling out and then killing himself, it had been an awful rough year on his Vice-President. Maybe he should go away for a while, take a trip. He was tired. It was two months or more since he had last got away. Those trips to the Coast or to Miami kept him going. Selma was on the Coast. Selma was a doll. With her he could relax, the way he couldn't at home. Yeah, but that was just because he didn't see her too often. That was the perfect relationship for a man and a woman. It was a lovely relationship. They trusted each other, they were good friends. He was good to her and she—well, she gave him what he needed. And it didn't hurt anybody. He was still a good husband and father. The one thing you had to watch was not to let it matter too much. Not to let it get too close. So that when the break came there were no hard feelings.

That was where Louis hadn't been smart. He let it get too close. Gloria was a wonderful girl, but she didn't see it right. She should have seen that Louis couldn't marry her. She should have let him be what he wanted to be—a wonderful friend. Louis could be the best friend anyone, man or woman, ever had. He would have done big things for Gloria. Only she had to spoil it by wanting him to marry her.

Harry had a very wide use for the word friendship. You were a good friend, in Harry's book, if you were sincere, and you were sincere if you wanted what was good for Harry. He spent a great deal of his time worrying about the sincerity of the people around him. Now his secretary, Ziggie Anderson, she was a good girl and she was smart, but sometimes he wondered whether she was sincere. He never knew where he stood with her. She was too smart. Whenever he asked her to go out to dinner, she always got out of it without saying no. At the time he never realized it, but he realized it afterwards. Now if she was sincere she wouldn't be like that. She'd realize that he could do a lot for her and she'd be nice to him. They could be wonderful friends.

And this new guy, this attorney fellow that had been put in —he wasn't sincere. He didn't fool Harry for one minute. Sure, he knew what he was there for. To watch him, Sarnoff.

The indignity of it. Sarnoff had helped to make this business, he had been Louis's right-hand man, and now he was being watched by a little pipsqueak fresh out of law school. But he didn't hold it against Vandenberg. After all, Vandenberg was new to the game and it was understandable that he would want to cover all bases. Vandenberg was smart, all right. After all, he'd been smart enough to keep Sarnoff as Vice-President even when he let the others go.

Reluctantly, Harry climbed out of the tub and began to dry himself. The lights in the bathroom were warmly gold, like candlelight. They made you look good. Even the white skin where the bathing trunks always covered him looked warm and tanned, and the rest of him was bronze. He stared into the mirror, pulling down the skin beneath his eyes and turning his head from side to side, observing his reflection. He didn't look so bad. Under this light he looked goddamned good. Sally didn't like the lights in the bathroom, because she couldn't see by them to put her make-up on, but he liked them. It made him feel young again, seeing his face without the little puffs under the eyes and the lines about the mouth. That young feeling was very important. It made him forget his paunch and the dizzy spells and the fact that he couldn't drink like he used to and the thought of the last man he knew that had keeled over and died in a heart attack.

He dressed in his lavish, aquamarine-blue dressing-room, and went downstairs. The kids weren't up yet, and Else, the Lithuanian cook, served his breakfast to him alone. Sally didn't get up to breakfast. He never got used to that. He didn't like eating alone, and lunch and dinner he never would eat alone, but breakfast foxed him. He never could get his wife or the kids to get up early.

It often seemed to him that wives were spoilt. Take Sally, now. When they hadn't had any money she'd been a good girl. She loved her children and she worked hard. But now things were easy it was different. She was still a good mother, mind you, but it was different. She liked her mink coats and her parties, she liked to lie in bed in the morning and she didn't worry about not seeing much of her husband so long as he took her out often enough. And she was tough on the help. She

could be a hard woman. That was why they couldn't keep
help. He shouted at them once in a while, but he was a soft
touch, and they knew it. They would stay for him. But always
Sally drove them too hard, and finally they came to him, tears
in their eyes: 'Mr. Sarnoff, we like you, we love your children,
you have a beautiful house here and you pay us well. But we
don't have to work so hard. We can get other jobs. Mrs.
Sarnoff she just don't know that.' There were a lot of things
Sally didn't know.

He was still thinking of wives as he drove to New York in
his smart white convertible. He liked a white car. Once
before, when he was down on his luck, he had bought a
yellow car—a bright, mustard-yellow Cadillac convertible with
red leather upholstery. It had done something for him. People
had looked at him and said: 'Look at Harry. He must be
doing nicely. Sure, Harry always does nicely for himself.
Harry's smart. Lookit, the car Harry's driving.' He still
remembered that yellow car with affection. When he turned
the corner he sold it, and bought a quieter one, but he still
liked light-coloured cars.

And he liked to drive. Driving along the elegant, tree-lined
parkways from Westchester to New York, he never got completely over the wonder of it. This is me, Harry Sarnoff.
Driving a six-thousand-dollar car from the best residential
section of Westchester to the best section of New York City.
Me . . . Harry the Bum. And he sometimes chuckled as he
remembered that nickname. He had got it as a young man,
when he was doing any job from bouncing in a Newark
speakeasy to acting as cover man for a gambler. Well, no one
had called him that in a long time.

Thinking of wives brought him back to Louis. If Sadie had
been an easier woman, maybe Louis wouldn't have got so
serious about Gloria. Of course, Harry knew Gloria was
different. She wasn't like the girls he went for. He recognized
that. He wouldn't have touched her with a ten-foot pole.
She was brought up like a good Catholic girl and she shouldn't
ought to have monkeyed with anyone like Louis in the first place.
But if Sadie had been more of a woman, maybe Louis wouldn't
have taken it so hard. And maybe he wouldn't have taken that

last train trip to Times Square. Who knows. Wasn't only the loss of the business.

When he got to the office, Ziggie was already there, putting out the trays containing papers from the previous day. Sarnoff was a great one for a tidy desk and he insisted on everything being locked up at night. They had confidential stuff lying around and he didn't take no chances, not Harry Sarnoff. Sometimes he felt Ziggie didn't quite realize the need for confidentiality and secretly laughed at him, but she was a good girl and she observed his rules. That was one thing he liked about Ziggie. He could feel safe with her. She might disagree with him privately, but he was her boss. What he said, that was final. And she was loyal. He had found that out when the big shake-up came. If only she'd learn to be a real friend.

'Hello, Ziggie.'

'Good morning, Mr. Sarnoff.'

'Sam in?'

'Not yet. He'll be late. Said last night he'd be going down to the law library.'

'Oh, sure, sure. I forgot. I asked him to look something up.' He looked glad. 'Ziggie, sit down. I want to talk to you.'

Obediently, she sat down on the chair the other side of his desk. She had her notebook ready. She always had her notebook ready, that was something else he liked. No waiting for her to find a pencil when he had an idea. He motioned the book aside.

'It's about Sam. He's been here nearly six weeks now.'

'Yes, sir.'

'How's he making out?'

'Pretty well, I'd say. He's a smart guy.'

He was watching her closely.

'You like him?'

With anyone else the question would be innocent enough, calling for a straight 'yes' or 'no'. But Ziggie knew her Sarnoff. She looked judicial.

'He's nice. Straightforward. Quick to learn. Of course, he's young. He still has a lot to learn about this particular business, but I think he realizes it.'

'You do?'

'Yes. I think he's very grateful for the chance to learn from you. It is, after all, quite an opportunity for a young man.'

He tried to conceal his pleasure at her flattery, not too successfully. He made an expansive gesture.

'I don't know . . . Young men usually think they're pretty smart. I think Sam thinks he's pretty smart.'

'But I agree. He is.'

'Ziggie . . . You know what I think?'

She watched him, watching the small eyes narrow. She liked Sarnoff, but she had no illusions about him. Perhaps because of that she could serve him as few other people could.

'You think Mr. Vandenberg put him here to—watch this office.'

'You ain't so dumb.'

'It wouldn't be surprising. You can't blame P. V. for wanting a finger on the pulse. After all, you know so much more about the business than he does.'

'No, kid. Make no mistake. I don't know more about the business than P. V.' But in spite of the denial, again his gratification was evident. 'Kid, that's one man who *is* smart. He's big. And he's a lot like Louis used to be. They're the same kind. Men with brain. That's why I don't mind working for P. V. In a way, it's like . . . working for Louis all over again.'

He spoke earnestly and sincerely. His self-deception was almost touching. She knew that he had really talked himself into believing that he had 'been persuaded' to stay on at Vermeyers out of sheer loyalty to his dead friend and boss. But there was no malice in her ironic acceptance of his pretence. She had come to know this man intimately in her four years of working for him, and she knew the good things as well as the bad. She knew him to be the most generous and warm-hearted of friends, as well as the most implacable of enemies, and she was content to take him as he was.

She guessed he had some purpose in discussing Sam. Finally, it came.

'Ziggie, I want you to be careful. With Sam, I mean. Help him all you can—I wouldn't want him not to do a good job,

[14]

you understand. But . . . well, I don't have to diagram it to you.'

No, he didn't. Sam was to get the treatment. No information. Apparent co-operation, but in reality a stone wall against which he would break himself trying to find out what the Vice-President did to earn his fifty thousand a year. Sure, she'd seen it before. When Louis Vermeyer had tried to get smart once and take over Harry Sarnoff's territory. Harry knew just a little too much to make Louis feel completely at ease, once they had come so far along the road. But Louis had known he couldn't do without the doctors, and the doctors worked only for Harry. So there had been the plant of the 'assistant' to take the load from Harry. Sure, take the load. The whole load, if Louis had had his way. And Harry would have been out, after eighteen years. Only it hadn't worked that way. Harry had come out of the tussle with a ten-year contract and an increase in salary.

If there were one reason more than another why Ziggie respected her boss, it was because he could hold his own in the jungle of East Side politics that ruled Vermeyers. And her loyalty to him was not complicated by any considerations of conscience. Any man who accepted the job of a stool-pigeon or spy knew what he was doing. It was fair game to try and frustrate him. Even if he were as nice and apparently ingenuous as Sam.

So she said now, understandingly :

'No, sir. I know what you mean. I'll give him any help I can and see that he—knows everything he should.'

They were a good team. He watched her approvingly, his small eyes twinkling. He liked to think he'd taught Ziggie all she knew. She was only a kid when she came to him. A smart kid, quick to learn. Well, a girl was like that. You could knock your head against a brick wall for years with a man, particularly a young man, trying to make him catch on. That was why he always wanted Louis to have a female assistant. That was one way to lick the problem of overwork. You could trust a girl. She didn't mind being just a 'right hand'. She'd never want to pull the rug out from under you and make herself the whole works, the way a man might.

But that was something they never understood. Louis never understood it. He'd thought Harry wanted promotion for Ziggie just because she was pretty. Well, okay, she wasn't hard to look at, but that wasn't all. She'd got a brain.

Sometimes the thought occurred to Harry that the cosmetic industry was a funny business. It was a business built for women, but it was still one place where a woman had a rough time getting to the top. Almost the only way she could make it was flat on her back.

III

SPRING had come to New York. It was in the fine fuzz of green about the young trees in Rockefeller City, it was in the high blue sky with the lazy clusters of white cloud drifting across it, it was in the soft warmth of the air that blew through open windows and ruffled the papers on polished desks.

Sam Woodstock walked up Fifth Avenue from the subway, savouring the warmth of the sun on his back and the light cleanness of the smell in his nostrils. On a day like this you could almost forget the petrol of the big city. This was a day when it was good to be a New Yorker. Although if you were Sam Woodstock you thought every day was a good one to be a New Yorker. Because Sam Woodstock, thirty-two, born in Brooklyn and graduate of New York University, thought New York just about the only place in the whole world where one could live.

It was a short walk to the building on Fifth Avenue which housed the executive offices of The House of Vermeyer. But he enjoyed the walk, he sauntered, lingering over it, that he might prolong the satisfaction that it still afforded him to enter the elegant building and go up in the lift and find himself in the lavish aquamarine and gold lounge that was the entrance to the suite. That lounge was a stroke of genius. You expected to step out of the lift into any ordinary office corridor, and instead the doors rolled back and you stepped out—into what seemed to be a feminine boudoir. It sort of hit you. There was an exquisite little chaise-longue set invitingly near the swinging glass doors, a full-length mirror faced you—an antique affair with baroque gilt leaves twining themselves around it—and the carpet underneath your feet was so soft and deep you wanted to just lie down and—well, just lie down on it. And at the far end, so that you saw it just before you turned away and went through the glass doors to the offices, there was a woman's vanity—a delicate, feminine thing clouded in organdie, with perfumes and cosmetics and a hairbrush lying carelessly on the mirror top, for all the world as though someone lovely and perfumed had just finished her toilette and gone out, leaving a faint aroma on the air behind her. Yes, that lounge hit you all right. Sam didn't know whether it was Vandenberg or Vermeyer who had thought of it, but whichever it was was a genius.

There were other marks of genius about the offices of The House of Vermeyer. Woodstock had never been in any offices quite like them. They made him think of the movies. He had been out in Hollywood briefly three years before, and somehow this had the same atmosphere of unreality. He always expected a camera crew to roll out and someone to start shouting directions to invisible stage hands and the whole fantastic backdrop to split wide open and show the rigs and pulleys holding the illusion together. And it never happened. Instead, beneath the unreality was a shining, efficient, steel-hard business machine.

Before Vandenberg moved in, Sam would have hesitated to join this outfit. Vermeyers, the most lush, extravagant company in the industry, would have been too flossy a venture to appeal to him. He would have said, long before the company's condition became known, that it was a risky venture. He wanted security. He wanted a chance to build a solid place for himself. He didn't expect to get rich quick. No part of his life had been like that. From the day when he sold his first newspaper to help keep the family solvent right up to graduation, he had had to work for results, and they had never been spectacular. But that was all right, that was enough. Give him a chance, he'd do the rest. No fly-by-night stuff for him.

Then Vandenberg took over and everything was changed. Vandenberg was the man who had put his mark upon the mail order business, the frozen food business, the airlines business, he was the man with the Midas touch. Sure, he'd started with plenty, but that wasn't all. He'd pick up a company no one else would touch, and the company would prosper. He'd go after an industry that everyone said couldn't be made successful, and it would succeed. He had flair. Sam had followed his career from afar. This was a man to follow. So when he got the chance to trade in his budding practice for a post as House Counsel at Vermeyers, he grabbed with both hands.

He breezed through the reception room, and Miss Adams returned his carefree greeting warmly. He was a small, tousle-haired, impudent-looking man and the girls liked him. He was friendly to all of them, and was careful not to be too friendly to any.

In his own office, he threw his hat on the rack and greeted Ziggie.

' 'Morning, Gorgeous.'

'Hello, Sam.'

They shared the room adjoining Sarnoff's. It was a very convenient arrangement. He was free to ask her questions all the time, and he could also see all that went on in Sarnoff's office, except when the door was closed. It was an arrangement that Pollovic, the Director of Personnel, had suggested.

'Where's H.R.H.?'

'Out. Back in an hour.'

Sam had a penchant for nicknames. Only Vandenberg was sacred, remaining 'Mr. Vandenberg' or, more rarely, 'P. V.'

'Did he leave me anything to do?'

'No. Just wants you to go through the mail. He didn't have time for it.'

'When do I get to real work?'

'Hope you don't. When you get to real work, we get to trouble.'

'Why do they need me, anyway, Ziggie? They never had this job before.'

She did not know how much this apparent ingenuousness covered. But she answered off-handedly:

'Oh, I think it's a good idea. We have outside attorneys, sure, but they don't take the same interest that you do. You can't expect them to. We're just one of many clients. Besides, they're old. I think it was a good idea on P. V.'s part.'

'It was his personal idea?' asked Sam, too quickly.

She glanced across at him non-committally. 'I wouldn't know.'

Sam sat back in his chair, putting his feet on the desk and

[19]

watching her. She was well worth looking at. He guessed her to be in her middle twenties. She was of medium height, and what would be described in the vernacular as built. Her hair was a fairish, golden-brown, loosely curling and worn very casually. The greatest surprise was her complexion. She had a fine, pale skin and she wore very little make-up. She was the only girl he had met at Vermeyers who did not look as though she had stepped out of an ad page in *Vogue*.

'You've been with Sarnoff a long time,' he observed.

'Four years.'

'Must know him pretty well.'

'As well as anyone, I guess.'

'You like him, don't you?'

'Yes. If I didn't I wouldn't work for him.'

'You're a funny girl. Some ways I can't make you out.'

'How do you mean?'

'You're a smart cookie, all right. I know how much you do for him. What I can't make out is why a smart girl like you wants to remain just a secretary.'

'I'm putting my widowed mother through college.'

'Quit clowning. I'm serious.'

'And I'm busy. I have work to do, my lad, if you don't.'

'That's another thing. You work too hard. They'll give you a golden tombstone.'

'Just think how pretty it will look on my wrought-iron buffet. . . .'

She returned to her typewriter. She wasn't typing from shorthand, he noticed, but composing as she went. Sarnoff didn't have to dictate to her. He simply indicated what he wanted, and she did the rest. Yes, they were a good team, he thought. She was Sarnoff's buffer state.

The telephone rang. Ziggie answered it.

'Mr. Sarnoff's office, Miss Anderson . . . Yes. Okay, Elizabeth. He'll be there.'

Sam tilted his head inquiringly.

'Name conference—eleven-thirty. That was Miss Shaw. Mr. Vandenberg would like you to be there.'

'Name conference?'

'The choosing of a new name for the Fall shade. You've not been in on anything like that?'

'No. Not yet. Pollovic told me Mr. Vandenberg wanted me to study all angles of the business.'

'He would. He's . . . quite unusual.'

Her eyes were veiled. He was suddenly curious. After all, he had been with the company less than six weeks.

'Ziggie . . . What's he like? As a person, I mean.'

She shrugged. 'I wouldn't know. We don't see too much of him. He puts in several days a week. He has so many other interests.'

'He never interviewed me personally. Everything was done through Personnel. I thought that was odd.'

'You're small fry,' she said casually. 'You would have to be a vice-president at least to rate a personal interview from the great man himself.'

'You don't like him.'

'I neither like nor dislike him. I don't know him.'

'What does he look like?'

'Fortyish, handsome—if you like your charm dug up out of a grave. A good man-of-distinction-ad type.'

She was just a little too flippant, and she did not look at him. So Vandenberg is attractive, Sam thought. Well, it fits with the legend. And he felt a sudden, surprising twinge of what seemed like jealousy. He wished he were not a full inch shorter than Ziggie.

'He's not married, is he?'

'Has been. Three times, according to the papers.'

'Must be rough—always to be in the papers. To have no private life.'

'I imagine if he wanted one, he could have it. When you have all the money he's got you can have anything you want.'

'No, you can't. Not the things that matter.'

'And what are the things that matter?'

'Happiness. Security,' he said surprisingly.

She paused. 'Well, security at least he has.'

'Not the sort of security I mean. It's a state of mind.'

She looked across at him for a moment, as though about to speak, then the telephone rang again.

[21]

'Hello. Yes . . . It is? Okay, I'll come along with Mr. Woodstock.'

'What now?'

'They're running a sneak preview of the new ad at the name conference. I am commanded to appear. . . .'

She made a gesture of obeisance.

He grinned. She was a good clown. And that was unexpected in a girl of her type. He had thought she would be stand-offish.

'What does that mean?'

'It means that a random group of people will have to commit themselves on whether the ad is good or not. This is something that P. V. started. It's usually a riot. Nobody likes to give an opinion before he does. Whatever opinion you give, you usually feel you've made an ass of yourself, because he just looks at you and says nothing.'

'He really operates a company, doesn't he? He doesn't just stand back and put the money in.'

'Oh no. He goes through it like a knife through butter. After the first month he seemed to know more than the people who had been in it for years. I don't know whether you saw— from the outside—what he did to our advertising.'

'I've never read the ads till recently—somehow I never used Ponds. . . .'

She laughed, then was serious again. 'If you'd like me to, I'll take you through the morgue after the name conference is over. On every ad since last June you can see P. V.'s fine Italian hand. Funny thing is, he does it all by suggestion.'

'Like Diaghilev and the lights,' he said unexpectedly.

'Lights . . .?'

Sam was grinning again. He liked to catch her off balance. 'You're not a balletomane.'

'No. Don't even know what one is.'

Her candour was refreshing. He murmured idly: 'Be good, sweet maid, and let who will be clever. . . .'

She couldn't think of anything to say to that, so she took refuge once more in her letters.

The Green Showroom was in darkness. At the door, Murray

Helfer, the little bald-headed Publicity Director, was moving nervously from one foot to the other. He greeted them with an effusive: ' 'Morning, Miss Anderson—Mr. Westbrook.'

'Woodstock,' corrected Ziggie shortly.

'Oh—of course, Mr. Woodstock. Silly of me.'

Yes, it was, thought Ziggie, because Paul Vandenberg was standing just beyond Helfer, and he had undoubtedly heard the gaffe.

He was just inside the doorway, in the shadows, smoking. He turned upon her a glance that was completely impersonal and expressionless. And his eyes were beautiful, in spite of it. She straightened her backbone, feeling the heightened colour in her cheeks, as though challenged by something in those brooding, unhappy eyes.

Woodstock saw both Vandenberg and the scarcely perceptible change in Ziggie's expression, and he thought: Oh damn. She really has got it. Quite seriously.

Then she was introducing him.

'Mr. Vandenberg . . . This is Mr. Woodstock. Mr. Sarnoff's new assistant. I don't think you've met him.'

The dark head inclined slightly.

'Glad to have you with us, Mr. Woodstock. I've heard a great deal about you from Mr. Pollovic. Good luck.'

And he smiled as he said that, the sudden, transforming smile that made his whole face come alive. Woodstock felt enveloped in the warmth of it, he felt inspired to do great things. (Afterwards he was to remember that sensation and feel exceedingly foolish, but that was afterwards. Just now he was enmeshed in this other man's personality.) He made an appropriate, undistinguished comment.

Then Vandenberg turned away, and they both felt forgotten, left out, somehow. Bea Bannerman of Advertising grabbed Ziggie's arm and shooed her towards a place in the front row. She sat down, grateful for the dark and for the silence.

Woodstock was thinking: That guy—he has quite a personality. But instead he said:

'This is better than the movies.'

She whispered back.

'Crazier than the movies. You're in the beauty business now.'

[23]

Bea Bannerman was shussshing them. There were probably twenty people in the room and they were all waiting in strained silence. Woodstock was consumed with a nervous desire to laugh aloud.

Then the door closed, there was a movement before them, and someone was on the raised platform just beyond the first row of seats. With a quick gesture, Paul Vandenberg uncovered something and pressed a button. Light flooded over an enormous colour advertisement.

It showed a girl writhing her way out of a deep armchair, wearing a low slashed gown and holding against the side of her face a bunch of grapes. The girl had the blank eyes and masklike features of a thousand glamour magazine ad models.

There was a subdued chorus of approval. Someone (Sam thought it was Bea Bannerman) gushed: 'Beautiful, beautiful . . . so devastatingly *sexy*. . . .'

Paul Vandenberg seemed to see all of them, in spite of the darkness. He spoke softly. His voice was deep, very quiet, almost caressing, yet with no warmth in it.

'Mr. Parker, what do you think of it?'

Myron Parker was Assistant Sales Manager. He was unhappy to be the one to lead off.

'Oh, er, I like it, Mr. Vandenberg. In fact, I think it's swell. Beautiful model. Beautiful arrangement. Lush. I like the juxtaposition of the grapes and the softness of her skin. Yes, I think it should go over big.'

'Mr. Liederman?'

'Agree with Mr. Parker, sir. First-rate. Got glamour as well as class.'

They all followed suit. And the chorus of approval echoed each pronouncement. Only Vandenberg himself gave no sign whether or not he liked the ad. Then Ziggie stiffened. He had turned towards her, and the quiet voice called her name.

'Miss Anderson. What do you think of the proposed ad?'

She stood up, her knees trembling. Because she was annoyed with her tell-tale knees, she spoke out boldly.

'I don't like it, sir.'

'Why not, Miss Anderson?'

For a moment, she hesitated. Then she heard her own voice saying calmly:

'I wish she'd either get into that chair or out of it. She looks as though she were sitting on pins. And she's too thin. She's wearing falsies, and you can tell. And the grapes—if she has to hold them, she should look as though she were going to eat them, not use them as a cleansing cream.'

In the silence that followed, she thought: I wish I might die. Or at least disappear. Her heart was pounding and her hands were shaking. She was fervently grateful for the darkness. Then Vandenberg touched a switch on the wall and light flooded the showroom. The silence was broken as twenty people began to cough or whisper or laugh uneasily, and they all blinked in the sudden brightness like surprised owls. Only Vandenberg was completely at his ease. He stood by the advertisement blow-up, looking at Ziggie and smiling a faint, sardonic smile.

He spoke quietly.

'Miss Anderson, you should be in Advertising. You have, it seems, an eye for the niceties of an ad.'

It was impossible to tell whether he spoke seriously or were mocking her. She was thinking confusedly: Why don't I keep my mouth shut? Why do I always have to be the one to say my piece? But at the same time she was stubbornly glad that she had not followed the herd. The heck with it.

Then Vandenberg spoke again. His voice was deceptively gentle.

'Mr. Helfer, perhaps you should take a vacation. I suggest Florida. It seems to me that you have forgotten what an attractive, healthy young woman looks like.'

Silence was absolute again. New as he was, Sam felt very, very sorry for the Publicity Director.

Mr. Helfer stammered ingratiatingly.

'You . . . you don't like the ad, Mr. Vandenberg?'

'No, Mr. Helfer. I do not like the ad. When we show a woman in an ad, she has to be a desirable woman. She has to be the sort of woman every woman would like to be. She has to have challenge, exoticism, mystery. She has to be something that a mother of six doesn't see when she looks into a mirror,

[25]

but wishes she did.' He gestured to a young man from Publicity who handled the blow-ups. In a bored voice: 'Take it away.'

And Sam found himself thinking irreverently of the Queen of Hearts in *Alice in Wonderland*: 'Of with his head, off with his head. . . .'

It was not a good day. The ad preview had been bad, and the name conference was scarcely better. Six names were put forward: Starlight Pink, Purple Velvet, September Orchid, Petal Rose, Fall Splendour and Fire Opal. Paul Vandenberg rejected them all.

'Mr. Helfer, Miss Bannerman, ladies and gentlemen. I wish to remind you that you are in the business of selling cosmetics. And when you sell cosmetics, you sell hope. You sell dreams and desires. You sell illusion. When a woman buys a pair of curtains, she thinks: That colour will look well against the wall and with my love-seat. But when she buys a lipstick, it's more personal than that. She thinks: This colour will make me look beautiful. She is thinking of some man who she hopes will kiss her. She wants to be desirable to him. It may be the boy next door, it may be her husband, it may be the butcher or the postman. . . . But when she buys cosmetics, *our* type of cosmetics, she sees herself lying on a bearskin rug in a transparent negligée, with *that* man wanting her. Mr. Helfer, do any of your names even remotely suggest romance?'

'Well, I think . . . Purple Velvet. . . .'

The Publicity Director's voice trailed off unhappily. Vandenberg continued relentlessly.

'Purple Velvet. So that suggests romance to you, Mr. Helfer? You surprise me. Now let me see—what does it suggest to my mind? Maybe my great-grandmother's best winter curtains. Maybe a funeral parlour.' He leant forward suddenly, resting both hands on the top of a table before him, staring into all their faces. 'Mr. Helfer—and all of you. You seem to have forgotten something that the man who founded this business never forgot. Mr. Vermeyer knew the origins of this business. Our success starts in the boudoir. If you want to continue to be successful, stay there.'

The quiet but resonant voice was more effective than shouting would have been. Sam felt himself caught by the magnetism of the dark eyes. And this man is new to all this, he thought. This is the man who showed the rest of the country how to sell to the farmer in the backwoods. This is the man who introduced champagne and oyster suppers on trans-Atlantic flights. The way he says it, it seems easy. Of course he's right. But how does he know so much about so many things? And how can a man of his intelligence take it all as seriously as it has to be taken?

Sam did not distinguish himself by suggesting a name. He was glad he was not in Advertising or Publicity or the advertisement agency. And when the meeting broke up, still nameless, Paul Vandenberg came across to him, a pale, slightly built man with dark, luminous eyes and an unsatisfied, sensitive mouth.

'I expect you wonder what this is all about, Mr. Woodstock.'

'Yes, sir. It *is* a far cry from the practice of law.'

'It's selling, Mr. Woodstock, whatever part of the business you're in. When you sell, there is only one rule: Find out what the potential customer wants a product to achieve, and then convince him that your product will achieve it. It won't, of course, because we all want the moon.'

IV

ZIGGIE ANDERSON was stacking dishes. She loved her small apartment in the Village, which she shared with a redhead by the name of Sharon Roberts, but she did not like the inevitable chores. As she piled the dinner plates in the gay, coloured rack, she was daydreaming. One day she would have a maid. She wouldn't have these greasy pots and pans to mess with. And along with the maid? A husband? Probably. It was still the only way a girl could achieve real independence. Being on one's own was all right, and being a career girl was fine up to a point, but there was a limit to what you could do on your own. It was too difficult to make a way for yourself. You couldn't make big money, the way a man could. With a well-to-do husband you could have far more of the good things in life. A house. A car. Pretty clothes. Oh, Lordy, how she wished she could have more clothes. The only difference between herself and the elegant women she saw on Fifth Avenue was money. She had a good figure, and her face wasn't bad. But she didn't have the clothes.

Sharon was playing the piano, badly. The two girls took it in turns to do the cooking and dishes. That way one day out of two each could enjoy the delight of leisure. And if someone dropped in unexpectedly, at least one of them was fit to entertain the visitor.

There were always visitors. Ziggie had never had to undergo the ordeal by loneliness that greeted most girls in New York. She had gone to college at Sarah Lawrence, and she had a host of friends from those days to launch her in her New York venture. She had been lucky and she knew it, just as she knew she had been lucky to fall in with Sharon. Her former college room-mate would have been a disastrous companion for her now, even if she had not married. Sharon was different. She was easy to get along with. And if she sometimes resented the fact that Ziggie had things just a little too easy, she did not show it often.

Ziggie knew things had never been easy for Sharon. She'd had to struggle for everything she'd got, and even so she had little enough. She was successful as a junior copywriter, but it was a hard life for a girl. And Ziggie knew better than most people how little Sharon's heart was in it. Her piano: that was just about the only thing that really mattered to Sharon, and she didn't play too well. Ziggie often speculated about that and was thankful that she had no desire to paint or play or write. To have the desire and not to be able to achieve it, that would be unthinkable. If you were Ziggie you had to do well anything you tried.

She put away the last glass, hung the cloth to dry over the rack, and took off her apron. One glance at Sharon's face and she knew that her room-mate was 'in a mood'. It was a not infrequent occurrence lately, and because she knew the reason Ziggie was sympathetic. Sharon was having man trouble.

'How about a movie?' she asked cautiously.

Sharon shook her head.

'We could play some records.'

Sharon laughed ruefully. 'Guess it would be better than my playing, at that.'

'You know your playing always sounds good to me.'

'Yes. You're tone-deaf when you want to be.'

Ziggie threw herself down in an armchair and curled her feet up.

'I should do some washing.'

'So should I.'

'Don't feel a bit ambitious about it.'

'How can anyone feel ambitious about chores?'

Ziggie leant back, stretching luxuriously.

'Had to take the new attorney to a name conference this morning. Vandenberg was there.'

'You're very interested in the big man, aren't you?'

Ziggie's eyes were half-closed.

'He intrigues me.'

'Why?'

'Perhaps because he looks through you. As though you weren't there.'

'He probably practises it in front of a mirror.'

'I don't think Paul Vandenberg has ever had to practise anything.'

'My dear, hero-worship is not much in my line. What's the attorney like?'

'Oh—nice. Short, intelligent, amusing.'

'Why don't you invite him round?'

Ziggie shook her head. 'Not anyone in our office.'

'Why not?'

'Sarnoff wouldn't like it.'

'Sarnoff hasn't bought you.'

'He gives me a handsome meal ticket.'

'Vermeyers pays you. Not Sarnoff.'

'Same thing. Without him, I'd be out. The way lots of the kids are.'

'You have an exaggerated loyalty to the man. You do a good job.'

'And he values it. My loyalty isn't exaggerated.'

Sharon snapped down the lid of the piano. She was on edge. Ziggie looked across at her.

'What's the trouble?'

'Nothing.'

Sharon's rigid back was expressive. Ziggie did not pursue the subject. Bet she's busted up with Jerry, she thought.

She wondered: What shall we do now, until it's time to go to bed? That was always the problem with the evenings. Some nights, when the gang came round, it was all right. They had fun. But there were always the nights when they were on their own. And lately these nights had been getting difficult. You either did chores or you bickered.

Although she would have died rather than admit it, Ziggie sometimes thought wistfully of her own home back in St. Paul, Minnesota. It had been a nice home, and there was something in being a member of a family that was absent when you were just two girls on your own. Of course, it was smart to be a big city girl, holding your own with the rest of the world, and it was nice to be free, to have parties when you wanted them, and have anyone you would come and go. If she were still home now, Mother would be fussing over her to get married to one of the local boys, and every time she went out Dad would be waiting up for her to make sure she got home in good time. No, it was better being on your own.

And yet . . . And yet. . . .

It was easier when you lived at home. Men didn't try to take advantage of you. When they took you out, they knew they had to meet your parents. There was something about New York that made it a man's town. It was too full of bachelor girls. When a man took you out to dinner he thought he had a right to go home with you afterwards. That was why she had decided, at the outset, that the only way to live was with a room-mate. Ziggie was no fool. She had no intention of living like a nun, but she had no intention of letting any man get away with anything, either. As she would have put it, she 'wasn't that sort of a girl'.

And she knew that Sharon was having trouble now with Jerry. Jerry was a very bright young man, a man who would certainly amount to something. So why doesn't he propose to Sharon, she thought with mounting exasperation? But she knew he wasn't going to. Ziggie had met Jerry. He didn't want to tie himself down in marriage. It's still a man's world, she thought, no matter what we do to try and make it otherwise. We can do a good job, we can hold our own, but it still pays to be a man. Damn their eyes.

The doorbell rang. 'I'll get it,' Ziggie said, getting to her feet. She was glad of the diversion.

She was less glad when she saw who it was. Standing on the doorstep, a package under one arm, was Sam Woodstock.

'Greetings,' he said cheerfully. 'I bring you roses. Four Roses.' And he proffered the wrapped bottle.

She had to laugh, in spite of her annoyance.

'Come in, Sam. Is this an official visit?'

'Is an official visit ever preceded by Four Roses? No, sweetheart, I'm here to play wolf.'

'Well, you're playing it at the wrong door. Grandmother isn't home.'

[31]

He had followed her into their living-room, and she was introducing him to Sharon.

'Sharon, this is Sam Woodstock. My room-mate, Sharon Roberts.'

'Pleased to meet you.'

Sharon stood up. 'How charmingly you lie. All men wish I were dead when they find Ziggie has a room-mate.'

'Ziggie has plenty of visitors, then?' His quizzical eyebrows went up. 'Pity—pity.'

Sharon noticed the glance he threw at Ziggie, who was certainly something to look at. She was wearing tight black velvet bull-fighter pants and a silk blouse with a high collar and a deeply plunging neckline that showed to perfection her small, well-shaped bosom. At that moment Sharon was irritated that Ziggie never wore a bra about the house. It seemed to her to be taking an unfair advantage of her natural endowments. Sharon was a tall girl and built to match.

'How about a drink?'

'Delighted. But what I really had in mind, if you weren't doing anything, was that we could go out on the town. I could dig up a friend,' he added hastily.

Sharon shook her head. 'Not in the mood. But you two go ahead.'

'I've a better idea,' Ziggie put in. 'Let's play the gramophone and make our own beautiful music. With your Four Roses, of course.'

'You mean you're just too lazy to get dressed.'

'That's right,' she said easily. 'I'm not getting back into a girdle at this time of night.'

'You know,' he said whimsically, 'there's something I like about a girl with her girdle off. Always seems to break down the natural reserves, or something.'

She said nothing to that, tilting her head and giving him a sidelong glance. Then she went over to the gramophone. Instead of putting on a popular number, as he expected, she had chosen a Brahms symphony.

As she sat down in the armchair, he nodded humorously. 'I get it. This is to keep me the other side of the room.'

'That's right,' she said again.

Over cocktails, they talked idly of anything and nothing. Abruptly, Sam looked across at Ziggie.

'If I asked you for a date, would you accept?'

'No,' she said bluntly.

'That's what I figured. Why?'

'For one thing, Sarnoff wouldn't like it. For another, Vermeyers wouldn't like it.'

'They don't buy your private life.'

'That's what you think. They frown upon friendships inside the office.'

'That's not what I've heard.'

'What have you heard?'

He had humorous brown eyes with little crinkles at the corners. The crinkles deepened now.

'Sweetheart, what about Gloria Vernon and the former chief?'

'That was different. They're—or were—high-ups.'

'Oh. So that makes a difference.'

'Sure. If you're at the top, you make your own rules.'

'I wonder if P. V. makes his own rules. He's quite a guy, by the way.'

'P. V. is above it all. He's like some—some visitor from another world. He doesn't fit, with people like Harry Sarnoff.'

And you don't fit, either, he thought. He had already noticed that the people at Vermeyers were not what he had expected. The old guard were mostly cut to a pattern— Sarnoff's pattern. It disturbed him. Among thinking, literate people, he could hold his own. Here he already felt at a disadvantage.

'What was Louis Vermeyer like?' he asked her.

'I never liked him. In fact, I stayed out of his way all I could. Most of the women were crazy about him. Talk to them now and you'll find they still get goose pimples at the thought of him. He was that kind of man.'

Sam had seen his photograph in the morgue. It was a compelling face. Yes, he could see where women might have fallen for him. But this atmosphere of semi-worship that still pervaded his memory. . . . Ziggie was right about that, and he just didn't see it.

[33]

'What I don't get is why people talk about him as though he were one of the seven wonders,' he said.

She shrugged. 'The Horatio Alger complex. Rags to riches —via sex. That's the story of The House of Vermeyer. Louis Vermeyer used his understanding of women to found a multimillion dollar business.'

He looked at her shrewdly. 'You're all wrapped up in it, aren't you? You wouldn't want any other job.'

Again the shrug. 'Beauty is a woman's field. Some day women are going to get to the top in it, if they're smarter than the men they work for.' She laughed at him, her eyes half-closed. 'But I'm just a girl who uses soap and water.'

It still seemed to him a fantastic business. It just didn't make sense. So much money from little pots of paint.

And he couldn't help wondering: Won't she be disillusioned? This is no business for women. It's a money business. That's why even Louis Vermeyer couldn't stay the course. When you get into those astronomical sales figures— brother, it takes an awful lot of potatoes to keep the thing moving.

After that, they danced, and then Sam danced with Sharon, who was laughing light-heartedly with the drink she had had and the companionship of this good-humoured little man. She was almost a head taller than he. Ziggie watched them, thinking of the line from the song, 'They're either too short or too tall. . . .' Well, Sam hadn't got what Jerry had, but he was a nice guy. Now if he could only get interested in Sharon instead of in her. . . .

And immediately there was another picture in her mind, a picture from a New Year's Eve party a couple of years back at Sarnoff's house. Gloria Vernon, another tall girl, had been dancing with Vermeyer, who was quite short. That had been the first time she had ever realized what was going on between them. She remembered now with some surprise that she had been shocked. Gloria had looked radiant, as though a light were burning inside her. Ziggie had never seen anyone look so beautiful.

She wondered what Gloria thought of Paul Vandenberg. It was a mixed-up world. People always fell in love with the wrong partners. And the Vandenbergs of the world came and went, and never even knew lesser fry existed. She would never be able to dance with Vandenberg.

Ziggie was getting sleepy with the whisky, and her thoughts were confused. She hoped Sam would go home soon. She had to wash her hair, and she didn't want to get to bed late. That was another problem of being a career girl. You always had to get up early and be bright and fresh and 'on the ball'. It would be so nice to be able to lie in bed in the morning and not have to face an office.

When Sam and Sharon stopped dancing, Ziggie was lying on the rug in front of the old fireplace (a genuine log-burning fireplace, which was Ziggie's pride and joy). She was asleep.

Sam grinned down at her, whispered to Sharon:

'Guess she knows how to tell a guy it's time to go home.'

Later, as he took the subway to his home in Brooklyn, he kept thinking of the way she looked, curled up on the floor, one hand under her face. Her lipstick was all rubbed off and she looked like a little girl.

She was different from the run-of-the-mill crowd. She talked the same language, but it was a language she had learned. Like her fair Scandinavian skin, the things about her that were not of New York impressed themselves upon him.

He began to wonder what her parents were like. This was a girl he'd like to know—in the good old-fashioned way.

V

'THE big thing to remember about Youth Elixir is that it is *not* a cream, or a lotion; it's a treatment. It's like nothing else in our line. It's like nothing in anybody's line.'

Gloria could hear her own words as they must sound to the bored women in the room before her. It's no good, she thought. I'm saying the things we agreed to say, but I'm not giving them anything. They aren't going over.

Too many classes were like that lately. She stood up there in front of the blackboard that made the room look like a schoolroom, and she drew her little diagrams and made her little jokes, but they just didn't go over. She'd lost what it takes. Perhaps if she could stop listening to herself it would come back again. In the old days, when this had all been one fabulous, fascinating adventure, she'd had it all right. Whatever it was. That quality that made the most commonplace words sound wonderful, gay, exciting. The quality that made the girls she taught as enthusiastic as she herself was. Maybe that was it. Enthusiasm. That was something that had gone out of her.

So she had a job to do. She had a cream to put over. Only don't call it a cream. Every house has creams—a million and one creams. This is different. It has to be different to make fifty million women pay seven-fifty a jar for it.

This was a class of demonstrators from department stores, and demonstrators were never easy. They were independent. They had poise and sophistication—had to have, or they didn't keep their jobs. They were exquisitely groomed, and just a little superior. Gloria Vernon, in the face of that indefinable hostility that certain women exude, put up her own barriers. She was never particularly at her ease with women. She preferred the company of men. With men she could relax and be herself. With women, she was always aware of the girl who had started all this, the girl Gloria Vernon used to be before she made the grade and became the Vermeyer girl. Long legs and awkwardness, poor skin, and hands that were always in the way. Funny. She hadn't thought about that in a long time. Only the demonstrators made her remember what it had felt like before she became a beauty.

One of the girls, a statuesque, incredibly languid blonde, was asking her about application. Gloria illustrated her answer with her hands, massaging the imaginary cream into her skin, patting very gently around the eyes, smoothing her throat.

'Remember, it's light. Light and fluffy. There's no pull, no danger of stretching the delicate skin. Since it's mainly a product for the older woman, that is very important. But you have to show them the correct method. Stress the need for gentleness, particularly in the area of the eyes.'

Gloria Vernon was Director of Training at Vermeyers. She had been with the company since she was a girl of eighteen. The company had been in its infancy then, and there were scarcely more than a hundred employees all told. She had tackled every job there was to do—manicurist, travelling salesgirl, demonstrator, even model.

That had been Louis's doing. He had noticed her one day, and called to her, saying simply:

'You're beautiful. You're what I need. You're going to show everyone what this is all about.'

That was typical of him. She'd been in the company by then for at least five years. She'd just been part of the furniture where Louis Vermeyer was concerned. But she'd grown up in the five years with Vermeyers. Looking back on it now, she could see it as though she were seeing someone else's life through the wrong end of a telescope. She could see herself evolving from the leggy, fresh-faced, already attractive kid into—the Vermeyer girl. The tall brunette with the dark wayward curls and the incredibly large, deep-blue eyes.

With a start she returned to her class. One of the girls was asking her something. That was another bad habit of hers lately, this business of getting lost in her own private thoughts and not quite hearing what people asked her. But what they asked was always the same. The questions were never new, after thirteen years.

[37]

'. . . I always have this trouble. Jean Narcisse has the whole line.'

Jean Narcisse. Yes, that was their main competitor with a product like Youth Elixir.

'You'll find some competition there, it's true. But your last sales bulletin gives you the answer. Youth Elixir is not part of an entire line, because it doesn't need to be. Youth Elixir cleans as it rejuvenates. First, you cleanse superficially, and remove on a tissue. Then you apply a second thin film, let it seep right into the skin, do its job overnight. At the same time that it is floating soil to the top of the skin, it's doing its wonderful work, nourishing starved, tired tissues.'

'But it's twice the price of Narcisse's Petal Bloom.'

'And it's quite different. Remember, don't knock the other line. Don't say it's no good. Petal Bloom is a very good cream—but this isn't a cream. This is an extract. This is a biological.'

The class dragged on. It was only a sixty-minute class but it seemed longer.

When it was over, she felt her body sag a little. Standing up there talking to the girls was a strain. She always wondered if they could see the unsteadiness of her hands and if they talked about the changes in her face. Every morning now when she looked into her mirror she noted the changes. The skin beneath the eyes was faintly mauve, with a silky sheen. Small dents had engraved themselves at each corner of her mouth. They were the marks that scarred a face that was always tense. Oh, sure, she knew the signs. She'd been studying wrinkles and tension marks and puffs of age fat for the past thirteen years. And now, at thirty-one, she was recognizing them in her own reflection. And it was too early. These were not due only to time. They told of sleepless nights and drinking bouts and boredom.

When the room was finally empty, she pulled her calendar towards her. She had a lunch with the cosmetic buyer from the leading department store in Los Angeles. Then two visiting V.I.P.s who had to be given the works during the afternoon. She didn't know who they were, but Sarnoff had called her. 'Say, Gloria honey, I gotta couple of dames. Yeah, yeah.

Important. I want you to make them up. Give them the whole works. Do it yourself, honey, don't put one of the kids on it. This is important.'

Probably the wives of some of his doctor friends. Or maybe a couple of visitors from overseas. You never knew with Harry. He was always meeting people. The funny thing was that *everyone* liked Harry. Politicians and impecunious relatives, actresses and housewives, eminent doctors and racing touts— all were his buddies and all mattered to Harry. She might get a call from him to give a lesson in make-up to any one of them. Last time it had been a high-school kid who was a friend of his daughter's. But if they were his friends, they were important. And because he was Harry, she didn't mind. Sure. Harry and she were close from way back.

So she had an hour and a half to kill before lunch. Well, she should get after her reports. There was a mass of paperwork that she was supposed to do, and lately she had been letting it slide. What the heck. Let Ginny do it. Ginny was smart about reports and figures. Gloria never had been good at method.

She rang for Ginny, one of her two assistants. Ginny was a rather pert blonde, in her early twenties and devastatingly chic. Gloria had chosen her because her figure was a little lumpy and even with her clothes sense she would never be a rival for her superior.

'Ginny.... How far behind are we?'

Ginny had her notebook with her, and she ran down some items which she had evidently listed.

'School Board—you haven't mapped out the schedule of lectures. Remember, we're going into the schools in Michigan next month and all we have planned is the first lecture. Both Liz and Clare are getting anxious about their itineraries.'

'Can't you take care of it?' Gloria spoke with obvious irritation.

'I can work it up—in fact, I have. But you've got to approve it.'

'All right—bring it in. I'll look it over. What's next?'

'The current promotion. We've a batch of correspondence needing answers.'

[39]

'I thought you were answering the letters as they came in?'

'I haven't had time. . . .'

'Time! Ginny, that's important. Don't you realize that?'

Ginny pursed her lips. Yes, your high and mightiness, I realize it's important. And that it's your job. Pity you can't get yourself out of the whisky bottle occasionally.

'I've been preparing the School Board schedules, also getting up the "Question and Answer" sheets for Youth Elixir. They have to be in by the end of the week.'

'Oh.' Gloria had forgotten about the question and answer sheets. She sighed and ran her hand absently through her hair. 'That's a very pretty blouse, Ginny.'

'Thank you.' Ginny accepted her compliment with the same indifference with which she accepted her impatience. She knew Gloria and understood her perfectly. There was only one reason why Ginny liked working for the Director of Training: one day she would inherit the job. On that point Ginny had made up her mind.

Gloria, who cherished the illusion that Ginny liked her, would have been a little disconcerted, perhaps, if she had known nfst how soon Ginny expected to take over. But Gloria never anticipated such an eventuality.

'Well.' Another deep sigh. Among other problems, Gloria was wrestling with a headache. 'What next?'

'Mr. Vandenberg has called for a detailed report on all the personnel who report to you for training. Brief personal history, your opinion on their abilities, record of experience, et cetera.'

Damn Vandenberg to hell, her superior thought bitterly.

'Is that all? What does he think I am? A one man Gestapo?'

Ginny shrugged. She was too discreet to be trapped into disloyalty to the President of the Company.

'He has asked for it not later than next Monday,' she volunteered.

'I've no time for such nonsense,'Gloria said irritably. 'What good will it do him? A lot of meaningless facts.'

She sat staring before her, appalled at the amount of work needing her attention and feeling not the slightest enthusiasm

[40]

for any of it. Ginny, after a momentary pause, snapped shut her book.

'I'll bring in the lecture list for the School Board. That's all done—only needs approval. We might as well get that out of the way.'

Vaguely Gloria knew that she was being organized and resented it. But it was difficult to resent Ginny—she was so damned efficient. Without her, Gloria had to confess, she would be lost.

Oh God, what I'd give for a drink. An hour and a half yet to lunchtime. And I have to wade through that confounded lecture list. And those letters. Damn Ginny. She should have been answering them. There must be a stack.

With shaking fingers she got out her cigarette case and lit a cigarette. It was the only thing that helped when she couldn't get a drink, and it didn't help much.

As she sat waiting for Ginny to return, she was thinking: There must be more point to life than this. Somewhere. There must be some way of making things matter, of tying the loose ends together. That was what it was like. As though, when Louis died, her life had split asunder into a dozen loose strands, and she was every one of them and none of them. Nothing she did was important, nothing reached to her inner awareness, and yet she was standing on the outside, all the time, looking on at what she did.

The work didn't help. It should have helped. People always said you could sink yourself in work. Yes, but perhaps they meant work that wasn't personal. Vermeyers wasn't just a job—it was Louis and her. Vermeyers had been the means of bringing them together.

At first, it had been just a job. She had been an ambitious youngster who had to get to the top, and nothing was too difficult, no task was too demanding. Then Louis had noticed her, and the whole world changed. The work had become a precious bond between them, something they shared that no one else could touch. He had always told her, first, of any new thought in his mind. He'd toss it to her, and she would catch it, play with it, throw it back embellished with her own bright enthusiasm. That had meant a great deal to him. He'd

[41]

told her, often, what it meant to him: 'Gloria, you don't know what it does for a man. To know that someone—shares all this. Cares about it. Eats and sleeps and dreams it, the way I do. Puts it first. It's the biggest thing in any man's life—has to be. Most women don't see that—Sadie doesn't see it. And, Gloria, that's why it's so wonderful about you and me. You see that. You understand.'

Oh yes, she understood. The business brought them together, the business kept them together, in spite of everything. When he wouldn't divorce Sadie, she would have left him, but for the business. She couldn't leave him. She couldn't cut herself off in one irrevocable move from everything that had made up her life since she was eighteen. She was trapped. She knew the business had to come first for him, just as it had to come first for her.

Looking back, seeing the pattern of events, she felt afraid. You thought you were free. You thought you were choosing your own road. But it was an illusion. You chose the route, but the destination was mapped out for you.

And now—what was the destination? That was the question that frightened her, sent her into a fit of jitters that made her grab for the whisky bottle. Okay, she had a job, a position. She was somebody. But she knew she was simply top man on the slippery pole. And because she'd climbed so high, the view as she looked down was not reassuring.

Vandenberg. The thought of his request came back to her, and she hated him. Vandenberg. The man who caused it all. The man who made Louis kill himself. The hatred she felt for him was so strong and savage that she felt her hands shaking more violently.

She had seen very little of him. He was naturally a remote man, and she for her part had tried to avoid him. She told herself that it was because he was responsible for Louis's death, but there was more to it than that. There was something else that she always pushed away into the darkest corner of her mind.

That first day, when he had come to Vermeyers, she had seen him standing in the reception room, chatting to Sarnoff and Max Heidt, General Sales Manager, and his back had been half turned towards her. And she had stood still, her heart pounding, feeling the blood leaving her face and seeing the room darken, because it was not Vandenberg who was standing there, but Louis.

Then he had turned, and seen her, and she had been introduced to the new President. And staring fully at him in the softly lit reception room she had recognized that it was merely an accident of lighting and similarity in build and colouring. The two men were not really alike.

But she could never forgive him for that. It wasn't enough that he had driven Louis to his death. There had to be this turning of the knife in the wound, this constant laceration of old sores. Whenever she saw him, fleetingly, in the corridors of The House of Vermeyer, it was as though Louis were alive again.

VI

PAUL VANDENBERG sat at his vast, walnut desk, and pondered. He was spending an increasing amount of his time at that desk, and he himself did not know why. Perhaps it was because this new venture would be his last. He did not deceive himself upon that score. He was very nearly through, and this bright, tinsel toy that he had won for himself would be his last amusement.

It was proving to be a very profitable toy and he could look upon his achievement with satisfaction. If he were to die now, Vermeyers could go on for many lifetimes, following his policies. The moment was ripe for putting in a new president and himself retiring to the background. That had always been his way with any new company. Stay right with it for the first year, go into every phase of operations, check procedures, watch key personnel. Then, when he felt he could safely do so, take a back seat and let a trusted key man take over.

But where, in this business, did you find such a man? This was no ordinary commercial project. On the one hand, selling cosmetics was too easy; on the other, each year one more cosmetic company was born, flourished for a little while, and then went broke. The right advertising, keeping ahead of the competition, understanding feminine psychology—these were the intangibles upon which success depended. And not one of the men he knew from any other field could cope with this particular combination.

This morning he was thinking not only of the problems of management, but of one specific problem which confronted him. He had asked Gloria Vernon to come to his office, and he knew that it would not be a pleasant interview. But he could no longer avoid it.

Vandenberg was of course aware of the story of Vermeyer and his Director of Training. It was a tale he had heard only after his acquisition of the company, and it bothered him. What a man did in his private life was his own business, but such relationships were destructive and he had small respect for a man foolish enough to get so involved. In this instance the twist to the situation made it difficult. It was not the man with whom he had to cope, but the woman. And for the life of him he could not see where such a sordid affair could sit right with a woman like Gloria Vernon. He had met her, briefly. He would have said she was fine and clean, the sort of girl at one time you might like your own daughter to be, the type of woman you'd like to see married to one of your top executives. Not the woman for a clandestine love affair with her boss.

Staring unseeingly over the top of his big walnut desk, Paul Vandenberg thought about that. He had used in his thoughts the word 'destructive', and he recognized that Gloria had been the one to be destroyed. Oh, he knew all the tales about her. That she drank, that she ran around with every man in the company, that her work was a mess. Yes. He was prepared for that. It would follow inevitably, given the prologue. So now he was faced with the problem: what to do about it.

He could say it wasn't his problem, but he knew it was. When you took over control of a company, you took over everything. You couldn't take the profit and forget the rest. You had to worry about the headaches. You had to solve the personal problems. Otherwise you were just an operator. Vandenberg prided himself on not being an operator.

The easy way would have been to tell her, right at the outset, that he no longer needed her services. There had been others he let go. It would have been considered simply a part of the general policy of cutting back, and it would not have hurt her. But Vandenberg was essentially a fair man. She had done a good job for Vermeyer and he could not fire her without giving her the chance to do an equally good job for him.

Now he had to face the consequences of that first decision, because she had chosen not to do a good job; she had chosen scarcely to do a job at all.

When Miss Shaw announced her, his first impression was,

as always, a physical one. She was too tall. Vandenberg did not like to find himself topped by anyone, least of all by a woman. But she was quite strikingly handsome, a graceful, willowy-slim brunette, with exceptionally blue eyes. He noticed also her general air of good grooming. She had not let her appearance go, at any rate.

He rose graciously, and indicated a chair.

'Miss Vernon, thank you for coming in to see me. I won't waste your time.'

It was typical of him that he should speak as though she had a complete right to refuse his request for an interview. His next remark was equally typical in its directness, and she clasped her hands so that he might not see how much they trembled.

'You know, I'm sure, why I asked you to stop by. I am far from satisfied with your work.'

He was seated behind his desk again, facing her squarely, and she found it difficult to look at him. For one thing, the light was upon her, while he was almost in shadow, and the dazzle blinded her. But it was more than that. Behind the desk, in the same position, in the same haze of half-light in which she had been accustomed to see Louis, she felt again as she had felt when she first met him. This is no stranger, but Louis.

It wasn't fair. There was enough strain in this meeting without that. She had been dreading it ever since yesterday at four when she had received the call from Miss Shaw. Oh yes, she knew what was coming. She couldn't very well not know. That was why she had gone out on the town last night, and she still had a hangover. Oh, merciful heaven, why hadn't she had the sense to stay sober and go to bed early? She needed a clear head now. That was why the light was playing tricks with her again.

She spoke in a defensive voice.

'What is wrong with my work, Mr. Vandenberg?'

'I think you know. If you wish me to put it into words, however, I shall be forced to do so.'

He leaned back now, one hand on the desk, still watching her, and that too was a familiar pose. It was the way Louis used to sit. The similarity fascinated her, paralysing her mind.

Instead of thinking of things to say, she was thinking only that his hands were different. His fingers were long and slim, where Louis's had been blunt.

The silence was heavy between them. She knew she had to speak, but she could think of nothing to say. Instead she sat and stared at his hand, as though it held an answer to the problems that had been going round in her head since four o'clock the day before.

He sighed, and shifted slightly in his seat.

'Miss Vernon, you've lost interest. You do your job as though it were mere routine. That isn't what made you one of the most famous women in the cosmetic business at an age when most women are just beginning their careers.'

He was speaking gently. She knew that he was trying to make it easy for her, but she would not take the opening. She retorted angrily, because of the memories he had awakened:

'There's very little to it *but* routine, Mr. Vandenberg. You teach a dozen girls how to apply lipstick, you teach a dozen more how to manicure their nails. The same old thing. Week in, week out. And then you go on tour and make sure they are all doing the same thing. I teach routine.'

He smiled faintly. 'That's true. My job is also routine. I follow a pattern. I examine a company, pretty much as a doctor examines a patient. I decide whether or not to—operate.' Again the faint smile. 'And if I acquire control of that company, there are further routines. But we both know, don't we, that that wasn't what I was talking about?'

She was not looking at him. She was staring at the wall beyond and to the right of him. He noted the tension of her mouth and the way her hands clasped each other. Finally, she said shortly:

'Perhaps I've lost interest. There's very little for me to do now. It's all done.'

'You don't believe that. Or are you trying to tell me that your department is so perfect it couldn't be improved?'

'You know I'm not.'

It was proving even more difficult than he had anticipated. Even as he waited, he knew most men would not be patient. She was making it almost inevitable that he should fire her.

[47]

As though she realized the impossibility of her own situation, she shrugged, and said, almost inaudibly:

'I'm sorry. But—it's either there or it isn't. I do the best I can.'

This was better. Now he could do something with her. He leant forward, bringing both his hands together. He spoke very quietly.

'Miss Vernon, nothing will bring a dead man back to life again. You are still young. You have to go on.'

Her head went up, and she looked at him as though he had struck her.

'Please . . . I prefer that we leave—personalities out of this.'

'Do you think we can? Is there any point in talking at all, if we do?'

She felt bewildered. People didn't do this. People never came right out and said to her: I know what it is. I know why you drink too much and why you've gone to pieces. Poor dear, you miss Louis so.

No. People thought that, and she knew they thought it, but so long as they didn't say it it was all right.

Vandenberg didn't follow the rules. He was an apparently reserved man, and she had not expected him to talk to her this way. Nothing about him was what she had expected. She was struck by his stillness. Most men paced when they wanted to talk or think. This man just sat behind the desk, looking across at her, into her, knowing what she was thinking.

He went on, deliberately:

'All right. Let's talk about this in everyday terms. You may think it's in bad taste. I haven't any time for the niceties of good taste. You're wrecking your own career and you are harming the reputation of the company. I could fire you, and then we would know that we had both failed. That's not what I called you here for. I want to make you look at yourself. Look back at the past year. You haven't done a day's worth-while work. You leave your subordinates to carry most of the burden. Please don't tell me that you take classes; I know you take some of them, and in those attendance has fallen off. People won't learn from someone who can't teach, and you can no longer teach. You've forgotten what it's all about.'

[48]

He paused. She was getting her second wind now. Her cheeks were pink, but she said quietly:

'Is that all you wish to say to me?'

'No, Miss Vernon. I wish it were. These matters—your failure to take classes, your failure to tie in training with new promotions or deal with correspondence—serious as they are, these matters are minor. You are supposed to entertain visiting firemen. That does not mean that you have a right to get drunk in public, particularly in the company of male executives of Vermeyers.'

She put up her hands before her face. They were beautiful hands, the fingers long and tapering. She was trembling violently, and he wondered if she were going to cry.

The buzzer on his desk sounded. He snapped down the intercom lever and said abruptly to Miss Shaw:

'No calls. I don't wish to be disturbed.'

Gloria knew she should be grateful for that. She could not have borne it if someone had come in then. But even as she recognized his consideration, she hated him for it. She did not want to be beholden to him. It would have been better if he had publicly humiliated her. That would have been what she expected. She sat there not speaking, hating him with a violence that filled her entire mind to the extent that even Louis was forgotten.

Finally, she knew that he was not going to say anything further. It was up to her. She said in a dry, choked voice:

'All right. What do you want me to do? Resign?'

'That wouldn't solve anything, would it?'

'I don't understand you.'

'Miss Vernon, I wish you would stop thinking of me as an—enemy. I'm not interested in your resignation. If I were, I should have called for it long ago.'

'Then—then what *do* you want?'

Instead of answering, he asked her a question.

'How old are you?'

'Thirty-one.'

'Do you think the world stops at thirty-one?'

'I . . . I don't know what you mean.'

'Yes, you do. We're back to where we started from. You

may consider it an impertinence on my part. I consider it a responsibility of my present position. I asked you to try to put the past behind you and forget Louis Vermeyer, at least in so far as your work is concerned. I am asking only that you try to do a job for me, as you did for him. I know how valuable you were. I know how much he esteemed your work. Can't you try—to see yourself as an individual in your own right? Not as someone who exists only in relation to another person?'

'You—you shouldn't speak of him,' she broke in. She felt foolish. She was nervously twisting a handkerchief around her fingers.

'No. I should pretend that he has nothing to do with this, I suppose. I should pretend to know nothing of your—friendship with him.' He spoke dryly, but gently. 'Miss Vernon, I repeat—would there be any point in our having this meeting at all, if all we did was fence with each other?'

Her head was throbbing. She was still not thinking clearly. She had braced herself for this interview, she had thought she knew what he would say: 'Miss Vernon, your work is unsatisfactory. You have forgotten how to teach. You drink too much. I very much regret that your services are no longer required.' Yes, she had known he would be blunt. He was noted for that. But she had not expected sympathy, and something very much like sympathy was in his eyes and his voice.

And then, of course, she did cry. She left the chair that faced him, stumbled over to the couch, and sat huddled in it, sobbing. He made no move to follow her, but sat still at his desk, his fingers idly playing with a paper-weight.

When she had recovered something of her composure, she sat there, not looking at him, hating him more for seeing her like this. If he had just fired her, that she could have taken. And now she wished she had the courage to say to him: All right, I'll resign anyway. She longed desperately to say it. But she couldn't. She couldn't afford to. She had too many debts. And she knew she would never get another job in the cosmetic business. Her reputation in the last year had gone abroad.

She wondered if he realized that, realized the position she

had placed herself in. Instead of speaking, she sat waiting for him to tell her she could leave.

Instead, he said quietly: 'There's a bathroom in there'—gesturing towards a door she remembered—'if you'd like to wash your face.'

She got up, without a word, and entered the small private bathroom. She did not have her handbag with her, but of course there on a glass shelf were neat rows of the company's cosmetics. As she laved water against her burning eyes, she thought irrelevantly: He uses a different soap. This isn't the soap Louis used. And she clung to that small difference, because there was so much that was the same, so much that hurt by its sameness.

When she returned, she was calm and outwardly poised, in spite of the redness of her eyes. Vandenberg was still sitting at his desk, not reading the papers upon it, doing nothing. It occurred to her that she was taking up a great deal of his time.

He had partly drawn the curtain behind him, so that the full light did not now fall upon her. Again she was aware of a small shock of gratitude, and because of it she said in a low voice:

'I'm sorry, sir. I'm wasting a great deal of your morning.'

He smiled, somewhat wistfully. 'I won't consider it wasted, if we end up understanding each other a little better.'

'What do you want me to do?'

'First, I want you to take a vacation. At least two weeks. If money is a problem——'

'It isn't,' she said quickly. She could not bear to be further indebted to this man.

'Well, that's fine. But I want you to get away. Right away. Where you can relax and have fun. Then I want you to come back, ready to work hard and whole-heartedly. I have a particular project in mind—I won't discuss it with you now—which I can only undertake if I can count on your help.' Again he looked at her with that direct, searching glance. 'May I count on it?'

Bewildered, she nodded dumbly. She could not speak.

He smiled again, and this time it was a smile without reservations. She looked at him and thought: This isn't right.

[51]

This isn't the way it should be. And he held out his hand to her, standing up at the same moment, and saying gently:

'Good luck. And if you need anything, tell me.'

When she had gone, he flipped the intercom again.

'Get me Pollovic.'

While he waited, he drummed his fingers idly on the desk, still not turning to the papers which awaited his attention. He was preoccupied with thoughts of the girl who had just left his office. He disliked scenes. His reputation for bluntness had grown as much as anything else out of his dislike of prolonging something painful. He had learnt that anything unpleasant is best got over quickly.

The telephone rang. 'Pollovic? Fine. I've just been speaking to Miss Vernon. She wishes to take a few weeks off. She has my permission to take a month. If she wishes to take less, she is still to be paid for a month. Is that clear? Good. Please make all necessary arrangements.'

Only then did he turn to his in-tray, and the matter of Gloria Vernon went out of his mind, as though a door had closed upon one room and another had opened up. Paul Vandenberg never tried to do two things at once. If he were interviewing a man for a job, he refused all calls. If he were listening to a complaint, no matter how trivial, he accorded his complainant the same courtesy. But no one entered his room without an appointment. Elizabeth Shaw, the woman who had been his secretary for fourteen years, was given complete control. Every appointment, even with his barber, was arranged through her.

He rang for her now and disposed of those items on which a personal decision was necessary. Then he glanced at his calendar.

'I shall be away for the rest of this week.'

'Yes, sir. And you haven't received the reports on the field test of STX-3 yet. I called Mr. Sarnoff's office yesterday and they were to have been ready this morning.'

'Call Mr. Sarnoff again. I want to see them before I leave and I'll need at least an hour to read them.'

'Yes, sir.'

'Better—get him for me now. I'll speak to him.'

She picked up the house 'phone and dialled, then turned to him.

'Mr. Sarnoff is out of the office. Won't be back till tomorrow morning.'

'I'll speak to Miss Anderson.'

She handed him the instrument.

'Miss Anderson, I was expecting the field test reports on STX-3. They were to have been in my office this morning.'

'Yes, sir. They are complete except for the West Coast salon reports, which were late arriving. I've just received them. It will take me about a couple of hours to analyse them and fit them in with the rest of the figures. Then they have to be typed up. You should have them first thing tomorrow morning.'

He liked her crisp self-possession. But he did not like Sarnoff's leaving so important a matter to his secretary.

'Tomorrow morning will be too late, Miss Anderson. I shall be on a 'plane for Florida.'

There was a slight pause, then she said coolly:

'Would you care to work on them this evening?'

'Yes—if that's the best you can do.'

'I'll try to get the reports completed before then. But I don't think it will be possible much before five.' He could hear the rustle of paper. She was obviously flipping through the sheets and trying to assess how long the work would take.

'Where is Mr. Sarnoff?'

'He was called out of town late last night, sir.'

'I asked where he was, Miss Anderson, not when he went.'

'I don't know, sir. He called my apartment but I was out. He will doubtless be calling again today.'

Still the stone wall. In the past year he had tried to break down that wall, and failed completely. Harry Sarnoff was the only man who dared do as he pleased with Paul Vandenberg.

'How is it that he left you to carry out this work? I should have thought it warranted his personal attention.'

'He has given it his personal attention, sir. He mapped out the report and told me where to fit in the West Coast figures.

There was no point in typing up the job twice. He knows I can be trusted to proof-read.'

There was no insolence in her words or her tone, and yet he knew she was enjoying herself. Even while he was annoyed, he was amused too. Well, Sarnoff had her well trained. And if he knew both of them, the reports, when received, would be foolproof. And he still would not know how much of the work had been done by Sarnoff.

You never knew with a man like Sarnoff, he thought. Outwardly a semi-illiterate, a tough, a poseur, he yet knew more about this business than anyone in it. Where Vandenberg worked by scientific precision, Sarnoff worked by hunch. Well, he conceded, that's why I keep him. I can buy Harvard School of Business graduates by the dozen. And in this game it would take more than a dozen to outwit Sarnoff.

At five o'clock precisely his house 'phone rang. It was Miss Anderson.

'Mr. Vandenberg, I'm sorry but we still have about a dozen pages to go. It's longer than I hoped it would be. I could get the report to you about seven, if you would tell me where to reach you.'

He glanced at his calendar. Appointment at the Waldorf at six-thirty.

'I shall be at dinner. Supposing you send the stuff over by messenger to my apartment.'

'I'll bring it myself.'

'That won't be necessary. . . .'

'I can leave it at the desk for you. But I prefer not to entrust it to a messenger. I know Mr. Sarnoff wouldn't like it.'

His eyebrows lifted slightly. Was he being put in his place by Sarnoff's secretary?

'As you wish. I shall be home about nine. There's no reason why you shouldn't have your dinner first. Miss Shaw will give you the address.'

He was still amused when he hung up. He liked someone who stuck to his guns. He had no illusions as to who would win if he gave Miss Anderson instructions that ran counter to her boss's.

Well, that was all right, too. You could only serve one

master. The clever people who tried to get around that fact ended by serving no one. He must speak to Pollovic about Miss Anderson. He remembered Harry telling him her last promotional increase had been over-ruled. Whatever she was making, she was probably worth more. He scribbled a note on his jotting pad, before ringing for Miss Shaw.

'Lock up, please, Miss Shaw. I shall be leaving immediately.'

'Certainly, sir.'

He wished he did not feel so tired. And he wished he did not have a dinner to attend. It was a charity dinner. He wondered why he had allowed himself to be talked into it.

He disliked organized charity intensely. He gave lavishly to many causes, but with only a cynical half-satisfaction. Well, perhaps some of the money went to the cause it was supposed to go to. And if he didn't give, it went to the Government, so what the odds.

There was only one sort of giving that mattered, that meant a damn. The giving that went with receiving, the creation of opportunity. See someone with something on the ball, give him a chance, let him make something of himself. Yes, that was all right. That gave you a good feeling. That made you think—perhaps it was worth while, making all this money.

But making money was something he couldn't help; it was a disease. It was like horse-racing for a gambler. You did it because of something in your blood.

And no matter what you made, you never enjoyed any of it.

VII

ZIGGIE put down the last page which she had proof-read, and yawned. She was limp. It was almost seven, and she had worked right through the day, not even stopping for lunch but munching a sandwich at her desk.

Grimly she thought: I could break Sarny's neck. It was not true that he had called her the night before, and he had not called today. It was a long time since he had pulled a stunt like this, just going off and leaving her holding the bag. And where was he? She didn't know. You never knew with him. Not even his own wife knew. One of these days, she thought, I'll be stuck for an excuse. There's a limit to this 'I don't know' routine. She wondered if it had fooled P. V.

But she felt happy. There were only very minor corrections in the report still to be made, and she would get the papers over to P. V. in time. There was nothing that satisfied her so much as tackling an almost impossible task and getting it done. And this had been almost impossible.

Yet, in the midst of her satisfaction, she was thinking: So what? I could be out having fun. I could be relaxing in a nice hot bath or having a drink before dinner. The way a lot of girls are. Instead, I'm hot and sweating and exhausted, and dammit, I have to have dinner with Sam to boot.

Sam had been very helpful, pitching in and helping her, not worrying about its being beneath his dignity as an attorney. Sam was like that. He did a lot of little things to help that most men wouldn't have done. But she didn't want to have dinner with him. It was as plain as the nose on his face that he was taking too great an interest in her. And what was worse, he had begun to ask questions. It was one thing to rationalize, to say to herself: If he wants this sort of a job, he has to take the consequences. It was another to look Sam straight in the eye when he asked her: 'Ziggie, why did they hire me?'

She wanted to keep out of this. It was no affair of hers.

Sarnoff had a right to protect himself, and Sarnoff was her boss. But . . . Sam seemed pretty much on the level, in spite of everything.

She cleaned up her face, and they went to a little Italian restaurant on Forty-ninth Street. Sam offered to take the package over to Vandenberg's apartment for her, but she refused. Over a bottle of wine and some delectable scallopini she felt considerably more relaxed. And she had to admit Sam was fun. She liked his light-hearted impudence. And she felt that he saw more than he admitted, so she was glad that he did not comment. Like this business of her taking the reports round. If he had pressed the point it would have been hard to find a reason why he should not relieve her of that small chore. She could scarcely deny that he was trustworthy. But . . . Okay, so she wanted to take them. She wanted to see where P. V. lived. Was there anything wrong in that?

But she wished she weren't so sure that Sam understood her reasons perfectly.

The zabaglione was as good as the veal, and they had a Strega to cap the dinner. She was surprised when Sam looked at his watch and reminded her:

'Sweetheart, I hate to break this up. But it's nine o'clock. If you still insist on bearding the lion in his den you'd better let me bundle you into a taxi.'

'Oh, Sam . . . I'd no idea.'

'That's the nicest thing you've ever said to me. You mean I actually made you forget the clock?'

'Not you,' she chaffed. 'Just the zabaglione and the Chianti and the Strega. . . .'

'Witch,' he muttered.

'That's right. That's what I said. Strega.'

'So you know some Italians?' he teased.

'Oh, lots and lots of them. I love 'em. I'll probably marry one some day and be a big mamma with a stomach, and a spaghetti bowl always on the stove.'

He laughed. 'You just love the spaghetti. And you don't cook it in a bowl.'

'How do you know?'

'Because my Mamma had a stomach, and spaghetti always on

[57]

the stove. My Dad changed his name from Farinesi to Wood-stock because he thought it sounded better.'

'Well, I'll be darned. No wonder you know such good restaurants.'

'Yep. Come by it naturally. Come along. I'll put you into a cab.'

The night air was cool and it felt good. It also made her realize how much she had been drinking. As he hailed a taxi and handed her into it, Sam stuck his head in the door.

'Sure you want to go yourself? You're . . . all right?'

She nodded, smiling and glowing. 'Thanks, Sam. I'm fine. And you're sweet.'

He gave her a demure kiss on the forehead, before she realized what he was going to do.

'Good night, sweetheart. Don't let the lion eat you.'

Then he slammed the door, gave the address to the driver, and stood back. She could see his impudent, somewhat mocking smile still staring after her as they drove off. Yes, Sam was a sweet guy.

Italian. So that was why he had so many brothers and sisters. He probably had a string of relatives hanging around him like leeches.

Alone in the cab, she leaned back, her eyes closed. She felt very happy. Wine always did that to her. Made her feel that the world was just one big happy place with exciting things just around the corner. Why did so many people drink cock-tails? She always drank Martinis with the crowd, because it was smart, but she didn't like the flavour. And they made her feel miserable. If she drank too many Martinis she got to feel-ing really sorry for herself, and once she had disgraced herself at a party by weeping unashamedly on someone's shoulder. She didn't know what she was weeping for. Just felt lonely, she guessed. She knew it was something to do with her mother and father. She missed them. Yes, sometimes she wanted very much to be with them again. But she couldn't go back. She'd die in St. Paul, after New York. She couldn't go back to that small, smug suburb they'd lived in, where everybody knew everybody else's business, and the only things to do were go to the movies, have dinner at the hotel, or dance at the country club. Everything was so predictable. If she were there she'd probably be married by now, and doing the same things her mother had been doing for thirty years.

Twenty-six. She ought to be married. Sometimes it seemed to her she would never get married. Sometimes she felt almost desperate about it. There was so little chance to meet the right sort of person. Oh, you met people like Sam and the rest of the guys she knew. But she didn't want that. She knew what she wanted—security. A place in the sun. Exciting friends. She didn't want to become just another suburban housewife in a small, brick, detached house on Long Island, with babies all over the place and a monthly tussle with the accounts to make them come out right. No. Better her present life than that. She might be lonely now, sometimes, but she was free. There was always the possibility of something—just around the corner.

The cab had stopped and the driver was looking at her and grinning and saying:

'You're there, lady. Or do you want a drive around the park?'

She sat up with a start, paid the man with self-conscious dignity (and overtipped him shockingly just to show that she was his superior) and climbed out. And then her heart began to race. She was going to Paul Vandenberg's apartment. She was going to see how the other half lived. One particular, fascinating segment of the other half.

Of course, she had told him she would leave the reports at the desk, but she had no intention of doing so. She did not rationalize why she wanted to hand the bulky manila envelope to him personally, but if she had done so she would probably have summed it up in some such fashion as: You make opportunities, they don't happen. . . .

Paul Vandenberg lived in a very sedate block in the sixties. The building had a lavish entrance, and a doorman who looked like a very distinguished general, at least. The luxury of it all might have been awe-inspiring to some. Ziggie, however, staring at the marble nudes, thought irrepressibly: Brrr! No wonder he looks so cold. . . . And her wine-inspired fancy pictured Paul Vandenberg cavorting about the crimson carpet in the embrace of a marble nymph.

[59]

At the desk she was examined frostily by a pale young man with pince-nez on the high bridge of a very aristocratic nose. Yes, Mr. Vandenberg was in. Would she please go up. Her heart was still beating erratically, and she wished belatedly that she had consumed a little less of the wine.

On the fifteenth floor, the gilded cage of the lift halted smoothly, and the lift man waved a portentous hand towards the right. Even he had the dignity of a reigning monarch.

'Fourth door, madam.'

She thanked him and walked firmly towards the door he had indicated. As she raised her hand to the bell, she tried to banish the laughter from her face. And at the same moment she knew she was trembling, and was furious with herself.

She was about to ring again, when the door swung open. Vandenberg stood on the threshold, peering at her. His face was flushed, his hair dishevelled, and his dark eyes appeared to blaze at her. He was obviously and quite disconcertingly drunk.

Laughter died in her, and she was at a loss for words. Then he smiled faintly, standing back for her to enter.

'Miss Anderson—please come in. May I . . . take your coat. . . .'

She followed him inside, trying to hide the shock which his appearance had induced in her. He was swaying as he stood, and as he motioned her to a chair he said abruptly:

'Please excuse me. I am—not well.'

He turned from her, lurched across the room and disappeared through a door on the far side. She sat very still, trembling, and yet wondering at the same time why it should make such an impression upon her. She had seen people drunk before. But she remembered how the story went: He never drinks. Takes milk at parties.

Slowly, she looked about her. The apartment was not what she had expected. While obviously expensive, it was furnished with austere taste. There were walls lined with books and a grand piano which dominated the room. She had heard that he played very well, and was suddenly curious to hear him. There were no photographs anywhere, and only one painting —a large Bonnard over the fireplace.

The door opposite opened and Vandenberg returned. He

had combed his hair, which was wet, and she guessed that he had tried to sober up. He apologized again. His words were quite distinct.

'I'm sorry. It was very good of you to break up your evening to come here.'

'That's quite all right.' She handed him the envelope. 'I'm sorry to say there's a great deal of reading matter in it.'

He took it, and she noticed how his hand shook. He smiled in an odd, one-sided fashion.

'Yes. I'm sure there is. And I'm very much in the mood for reading, at the moment.' He stared at her. ' Don't you think I'm in the mood for reading?'

Searching for something to say and feeling profoundly uncomfortable, she said uncertainly:

'I hope the dinner was pleasant.'

'The dinner was most unpleasant. Charity dinners are always unpleasant.'

He turned from her, towards a wide couch, and sank into it with an untidy, shambling movement. It reminded her of a puppet collapsing on the floor when the strings are let go.

For a moment he sprawled against the cushions, his head back and his eyes closed. Everything about him was so different from the immaculate, self-contained man whom she saw in the Fifth Avenue office that she felt: This can't be real. This is a dream.

He opened his eyes and stared at her. His direct, penetrating scrutiny looked wild, now. She thought: If I were to be told he was mad, I would believe it. He looks mad. But perhaps— that's the way some people are when they've been drinking. I've never seen anyone drunk before except at a party, having fun.

The quietness of this room and the solitude of the man before her was unbelievably horrifying. Intuitively, she knew: When you drink alone, in a place like this, that is different.

'You wanted to come here, didn't you?' he asked her sardonically. 'You weren't just being Mr. Sarnoff's very efficient young lady. You were curious.'

Some instinct prompted her not to lie to him. She answered calmly:

'And if I were?'

'You were unwise. I hold women cheap.'

For the first time, it occurred to her to be afraid. There was about him always a remote, unfathomable quality, but now it was heightened. She did not know what she expected him to do, but anything he did would have seemed entirely logical.

She stood up, trying to hide what she felt.

'Well . . . I expect you want to get on with the reports. I'll say good night. . . .'

He laughed, unexpectedly. He did not move, but still lounged against the back of the couch, looking up at her.

'Afraid?' he said softly.

She returned his glance unflinchingly.

'Possibly,' she answered.

That seemed to amuse him further.

'Come here,' he said, one hand indicating the couch beside him.

'I'm sorry. I have to go.'

She began to move towards the door, but could not, without being obvious, avoid passing close to him. As she moved, he reached up, catching hold of her forearm, and pulled her towards him with a grip so strong that she sat down suddenly and ungracefully.

She was terrified now. If he were sober, she would not have been afraid of him. But there was something bestial and uncontrolled about his loose movements, and the grip on her forearm warned her of his strength. Involuntarily she looked around. There should be someone else there—a man-servant, at least.

As though he read her thoughts, he said slowly:

'There's nobody here. I live entirely alone. I like it that way.'

At that, surprisingly, calm returned to her. She stared quite coolly into his face.

She had never been so close to him before. Facing the challenge of his eyes, she saw also the fine bones, the well-shaped head, the slim, graceful hands. And she saw more than that. She remembered an Irish story about a man with death in his face. And this man had death in his face. It sat there and mocked at her.

'What do you want of me?' she asked quite calmly.

'Isn't it rather what you want of me? You wanted to see where I lived, didn't you? You wanted to see what it felt like to be in the same room with sixty million dollars. Well. How does it feel to be on the same couch with sixty million dollars?'

'You really don't like women, do you?' She spoke slowly, almost wonderingly.

He closed his eyes, smiling. He seemed very tired. 'Women,' he said, his voice very soft, almost gentle, 'women want only two things of a man. And the one that is most important to them is money. If you have that, they'll even forget about the other. They can get that elsewhere.'

She felt revolted. She watched him with the same fascination that she might feel staring at a wound. She was trying to reconcile the man before her with what she had known previously. There had always been about him before a quality of dignity, of power held very firmly in check. She remembered the name conference, and the moment when his dark, disenchanted gaze met hers. Now—this was the same man, this flushed, wild-eyed creature whose fingers were like a vice upon her arm.

Then he let go her wrist, sat up, and rubbed his eyes with both hands.

'Miss Anderson. There is a decanter on the sideboard. Will you kindly pour each of us a glass of brandy.'

She was relieved to find that his voice was once more as she knew it: suave, low-pitched, impersonal.

She hesitated. 'Mr. Vandenberg . . . Do you think you should. . . .'

'Miss Anderson, I know I shouldn't. But please do as I tell you.'

Even in this moment of physical frailty, there was an imperious quality in his manner that brooked no refusal. She did as he bade her, and returned to her seat beside him.

He drank slowly, savouring the brandy. When he looked at her again, his eyes were still wild. He chuckled suddenly.

'Are you Sarnoff's mistress?'

In the setting of this unreal evening, the question seemed quite normal. She answered simply:

[63]

'No.

'How do you hold him off?'

Her glance was quite steady.

'I do my job. I assure you, it doesn't involve any—athletics.'

Again he chuckled. She realized at that moment that, drunk though he was, his face was animated and human in a way that she had never seen it before. She realized, too, that he was a very attractive man.

He shrugged. 'You're discreet. Well, he's fortunate. It doesn't matter to me if he sleeps with you. Please get me another brandy.'

'Mr. Vandenberg—I have to go now. It's getting late. . . .'

'Miss Anderson, you will go when I tell you to go. Kindly get me another brandy.'

He held up his glass to her. She took it, and he smiled up at her. It was a challenge and she knew it. She was angry and excited at the same moment, and deep inside something was telling her : Whatever this man wants, he can have. And he knows it. He is used to having his own way.

She brought him another brandy, but left her own glass unfilled. He noticed it. He gestured, airily.

'Drink up. Don't have to be afraid of me. Wouldn't be much use to you tonight. Economy—have to practise economy. Drink—no women. Women—no drink. To hell with women, anyway.' He tilted the glass to his lips, then saw she still was not drinking. 'Drink up, damn you.'

She answered very calmly: 'I don't want any more. And I'm not afraid of you.'

It was now true. The fear had gone, and in its place was a compassion that moved her almost to tears. She could not explain what she felt. A line from *Hamlet* ran unceasingly in her head. 'Like sweet bells, jangled, out of tune and harsh. . . .' Inconsequentially, she thought: When he smiles, everything about him changes. His face becomes—sad, wise, not disillusioned so much as . . . the face of someone who never had any illusions.

And that is it, she thought. That is what there is always about him. That air of 'You cannot shock me or move me or hurt me, I am beyond it all'. That is what I've felt, when I looked at him. Being with him is like—knocking on a door that doesn't open.

He seemed to be interested in her. He sat sideways, with one arm along the back of the couch, sipping his drink and studying her profile.

'Miss Anderson . . . You must have a first name.'

'Sigrid.'

His scrutiny was hard to bear, and she could feel her heart thumping, but she would not look at him, now.

'Beautiful name,' he said unexpectedly. 'You Swedish, Sigrid?'

'I was born here. But my grandparents were Swedish.'

'You are quite—beautiful. Yourself.' He said it musingly, not as a man who pays a compliment to a woman. 'That dress suits you. Did you wear it specially for me?'

It was one of her favourites and it was a mere accident that she was wearing it today. But she prevaricated.

'I had a dinner date. There are a few other men in New York.'

He smiled. 'You left him early. He must have been disappointed.'

That made her feel foolish. She could think of nothing to say.

He stared into his empty glass for a moment, apparently pondering something. Then he rose, crossed the room unsteadily and brought back the decanter. He poured a drink for each of them.

Looking at him now that he was not watching her, she put out a restraining hand.

'Please. You'll make yourself ill.'

He looked at her in surprise. 'Yes. That's why I don't drink. Can't keep it down. My ulcer is my best friend. But for that I'd probably drink myself to death. Just a bottle—a friendly little bottle. And then a neat heart attack. So simple. No need for pills or anything that would look bad in the newspapers.'

The quiet, matter-of-fact words appalled her. Again pity and surprise filled her. She found herself thinking: He is not—

[65]

what I thought he would be. Tears were in her eyes, and to hide them she reached for her glass and drank slowly.

'Sigrid.'

'Yes?'

'Why are you crying?'

She shrugged, smiling self-consciously in spite of the tears. 'Probably—had too much wine with my dinner.'

'Women can always cry. One of their best weapons. Isn't it a useful weapon, Sigrid?'

She did not reply, and he put his fingers beneath her chin, tilting her face so that he could look full into it; then, still holding the brandy glass in his other hand, he kissed her, forcing her head back against the couch.

The kiss had nothing in it of tenderness. It was hard, angry, and animal. He put all his contempt for women into it. She closed her eyes and he laughed.

'Are you afraid of me, Sigrid?'

'No.' It was merely a whisper.

'You'd stay if I asked you to, wouldn't you?'

She shook her head. The ironic voice went on.

'Yes, you would. You're all the same. You always say no. Just often enough. But the final yes is always the same.'

This was a nightmare. She wanted to get away from him, yet she was afraid to move. Then, as she threw him a quick, despairing glance, she saw the intensity of his gaze cloud. The colour drained out of his face and he started up.

She tried to help him, but he pushed her side.

' 's all right. Manage by myself.'

He lurched away from her, across the room and through the door. For a moment she stood undecided, and she heard a door slam in the room beyond and a toilet flush.

For what seemed an eternity she waited. Then she went over to the door and knocked. There was no answer. As she hesitated, she heard a crash, as though something had been knocked over.

She knocked again, then opened the door and went in. Vandenberg was half-sitting, half-lying on his bed, a shattered bedside lamp on the floor. His face was contorted with pain.

She came close to him and he pointed to the floor. By the

[66]

pieces of china was a small bottle of pills. She picked it up, dashed into the bathroom, and came back with a glass of water. He motioned aside the water, but took the pill she gave him and put it under his tongue.

She was shaking. Mechanically, she picked up the pieces of the broken lamp and put them on the night table. Then she pulled up a chair, close to the bed, and sat and watched him.

At first he did not move. His eyes were closed, and she wondered, in a trembling, sickening horror, if he might be dying. But gradually his hands unclenched and the agony went out of his face. She lifted his legs, placing them on the bed, and shifted his head so that it was supported by the pillow. Then she waited again.

The wait seemed endless, but it was less than half an hour. He opened his eyes, smiled at her, and said:

'Thank you.'

'Are you all right?' she whispered.

'I shall be, very shortly.' It seemed an effort for him to speak, but after a while he said: 'I've kept you a long time.'

'Please don't worry about that. Would you like me to stay with you?'

The dark eyes flickered with a spark of humour.

'Coals of fire, little Sigrid. . . . No, thank you. I shall be all right.'

Five minutes later he had recovered sufficiently to sit up. She insisted on helping him to undress, to his wry amusement. He accepted her ministrations without embarrassment, and for her part she was too concerned for him to be aware of any oddness in the situation.

When he was comfortably established in bed, she asked him uncertainly:

'Mr. Vandenberg. If I hadn't come in when you knocked over the lamp—what would have happened?'

Again the humour flickered in his eyes.

'The House of Vermeyer would have had yet another president.'

Her limbs shook, as though a fever had seized her. She had never before been near to death. He saw it, and grasped her hand, giving it a little shake.

'Don't worry. I'll be good now. If I'm careful, I'll make my half-century. That's enough for any man.'

Unexpectedly, she raised his hand, placing it against her cheek. Her eyes were swimming in tears as she said chokingly:

'Please. . . . Don't talk that way.'

He raised a surprised eyebrow. 'You're crying again. Why on earth should you be? Over—me?'

It seemed unduly puzzling to him. He shifted his head impatiently and, as she did not speak, said abruptly:

'It doesn't matter. I'm not important. Not to anyone.'

Then he closed his eyes, as though very tired, and seemed to sleep.

VIII

ZIGGIE herself did not know why she felt so personally involved. As she let herself out of the apartment and walked over to Fifth Avenue, where she would take the bus to Washington Square, she asked herself: Why do I feel this so intensely?

She was aware that many of the women who worked in his new company regarded Paul Vandenberg with an admiration that bordered on hero-worship. She had herself been teased by Sharon for her own interest in him. But that interest had been a casual thing, or so she thought. He was simply a phenomenon —an attractive, wealthy, legendary person too remote ever to become a part of her life, although too constantly on the fringes of it to be disregarded. But now she found herself remembering the sombre, glowing warmth of his eyes, and the electric quality of his touch when his hands met hers. She remembered, above all, his kiss. Her cheeks were hot as she remembered it.

And she had prayed for him. Perhaps that was the most shattering thing of all. As she sat and watched, she had prayed: Please God, let him be all right. Only let him be all right. She couldn't remember praying in years. But she had prayed for Paul Vandenberg.

Sigrid Anderson had led a sheltered life. Her greatest adventure had been leaving home and coming to live in New York, and even that had been a limited adventure, because she had always known she could return if things didn't work out. That background of comfort and stability, the knowledge that her family was always there if she needed it, gave her a good, warm feeling when she thought about it. And because of it, perhaps, she felt no need of other props. She had done well in New York, and she prided herself on her own level-headedness. She wasn't a fool to go overboard in any of the ways a girl on her own could go overboard in this city.

But now she was shaken. She felt emotional and upset. She wanted to cry and did not for the life of her know why.

At a drug store, she paused, then entered, seeking a telephone. She knew that Vandenberg was attended by a Dr. Ernest Hammacher—she had had to call him for Sarnoff once when P. V. was taken sick. She sought and found his home number in the telephone directory.

'Dr. Hammacher, please. Oh, Doctor, this is Miss Anderson —Mr. Sarnoff's secretary. I've just left Mr. Vandenberg—I had to take some papers to him. While I was there, he became very ill. Yes, at his apartment. He had just come in from a dinner. I think it may have been too much for him.'

Dr. Hammacher promised he would go over right away. He sounded disturbed. Ziggie wondered whether she had done the right thing. Vandenberg would probably consider her a meddler. Well, better that than that he should have another attack, alone.

She did not take the bus, after all. She walked home. She walked home thinking of death, and of Paul Vandenberg, and of the loneliness that she had seen in his face. Even when she lay in bed that night, she was still thinking of him, remembering the quietness of his apartment, the vastness of the rooms that seemed so much too large for one man to live in.

Dr. Hammacher found Vandenberg calm, but wakeful. He noticed the smell of brandy, but said nothing. He knew his patient.

'I suppose Miss Anderson sent you.'

'Yes. Called me when she left here.'

'I didn't tell her to.'

'Glad she did. You need a sedative.'

His own sickness disgusted Vandenberg. He was not a natural pill-taker, and Hammacher's little bottles were a necessary but hated part of his life. It should have been possible to manage matters with more dignity, he thought.

'Tonight I nearly did it,' he said suddenly.

'Brandy is one sure way.'

Vandenberg smiled. 'Not sure enough. Can't keep it down. Perhaps, if I could. . . .'

The doctor's expression was calmly professional.

'Wasteful, Mr. Vandenberg. Don't you think so?'

'One last extravagance. Why not? Who is there to care?'

'There's always your boy.'

'I don't know him very well, Ernie. To be honest, I don't think he'd miss me at all.'

Hammacher sat and watched him for a moment silently. He had been Vandenberg's physician for many years, and he still did not understand him. A man with his fine brain, his many talents, wasting himself like this. . . . To Ernest Hammacher, it was little short of criminal. But he attended many wealthy men. Yes, that was the way it was. If you had too much money, something else seemed to go out of life.

'You should get away. You've been overdoing it.'

'I was planning on leaving tomorrow. A few days in the sun will set me up.'

'Better postpone it a couple of days. But stay in bed. You need rest.'

Vandenberg smiled, twistedly.

'Rest. I can't rest. I get bored.'

'Would you like me to send for your son?'

'Why do you keep talking of Laurie? What has he to do with it?'

'You need an interest. You need someone here, with you. I think you should get to know your boy better.'

Vandenberg gestured irritably.

'He annoys me. Too damn much like his mother. I don't want him around.'

His eyes closed. His son's face floated before him, briefly— a darkly handsome but effeminate face, weak where his own was strong. Then it faded, until it was not his son's face at all, but that of Louise, his third wife. Snob. A goddamned snob from Boston. A cold, calculating woman who married him for his money, but gave him a son. That was the rich part of it. The only one of his three wives to give him a son. And she was as cold as yesterday's mashed potatoes, as the song had it. He smiled faintly at the irony of his son's parentage.

[71]

Hammacher took his pulse and sounded his heart, observing him closely. The drugs were taking effect and soon he would be asleep.

Gently the physician packed up his bag, mentally thanked God that He had seen fit to make him just an averagely well-to-do man and a good, plodding doctor, and quietly left the apartment.

Meanwhile, the sick mind of Paul Vandenberg tossed uneasily in the dark world of dreams.

★　　　★　　　★

There were three marriages. And out of three marriages you would expect one at least to leave something behind it. One of the three women who had sworn to love, honour and obey him should have left some savour, some warmth, some tenderness behind her.

But none of them had. They had left so little, he found it hard to remember them clearly. Margot, the first, was the brightest image. Margot with the red hair and the beautiful white body. But perhaps that was because she was the first. Not only the first wife, but the first woman. He had been twenty, and she twenty-two. It amazed him sometimes to think that she could have been the first, and he twenty.

Although he scarcely remembered it now, he had met her on his father's yacht. She had come with someone—he never found out who it was or what she was in relation to him. His father's yachting parties were like that. There were always people he didn't know, and usually his father disappeared somewhere before the night was through, and the guests sorted themselves into couples and drifted into private places, or places they hoped would be private. The youthful Paul had found such parties embarrassing. Usually he was careful to stay up on deck once the drinking was under way. That was how he met Margot.

She was standing by the rail, watching the moonlight on the waves. It was a lovely, still night. At the time he had been much impressed by that, and by the warm glow of her hair in the pale brilliance of the moon She had seemed to him part of the clean saltness of the water and the coldness of the night, not of the party below deck. (And that was very funny, in view of what he knew about her afterwards.)

'You don't like the party?' he asked her.

'No. They're all getting drunk.'

She seemed very young, and he thought she was embarrassed by it, too.

'We don't have to go down. We could just stay up here, if you'd like that.'

'Yes. It's beautiful up here. It must be wonderful, to own a boat.'

'It's all right. Save that if you have one, you always give parties. And people get drunk.'

She stared at him.

'This is—your boat?'

'My father's.'

'Oh.' She looked at him for a long time. 'Then you're Paul Vandenberg.'

'Yes.'

Her face changed. Even in the moonlight, he could see the way her eyes had widened. And when she spoke there was a new note in her voice. A note of breathlessness, excitement— what he was later to think of as a woman's typical reaction to the magic of his father's name. But now that thought did not occur to him. He simply thought that she looked even prettier than a moment before.

'You don't like to drink,' she said, as though that were surprising in view of his avowal.

'No, I can't. It makes me throw up.'

'Oh.'

He could not be sure, but he felt his confession had diminished him in her eyes. He wanted suddenly to be away from the party and the noises of the boat.

'Do you swim?' he asked her.

'Yes.'

'Could you swim to shore?'

She stared at the shore-line, moving gently up and down ahead of them.

'Oh, sure. That's not far.'

[73]

To him, it seemed very far, but he would not admit it to this girl.

'There are always swimsuits on board. Wait here. I'll find some.'

She laughed. 'What a funny boy you are. Why do you want to swim to shore in the middle of a party?'

He did not look at her. He did not like being laughed at.

'Oh—I just thought it would be nice. Beyond that landing stage that you can see—beyond the reeds—there's a sort of—park. It isn't really a park, it's what's left of an old estate. There is a ruined house there. At night, it's very still, and you can lie in the long grass and see the glowworms and . . .' He broke off. 'But you probably wouldn't like it, anyway.'

'Yes,' she said, too quickly. 'I would. Find me a bathing suit and a place where I can change.'

Again he saw the excitement in her manner. It infected him. His heart was thumping as he went below.

That first swim in the moonlight had been the beginning of it. She swam superbly—better than he. He was in fact an exceedingly poor swimmer, but he drove himself to a sport which he actually feared. When they waded ashore, he had never seen anything more beautiful than her slimly rounded, gleaming limbs shining in the moonlight. He showed her the ruined house, and they lay side by side in the long grasses, watching the glowworms and the moon and the low, swift-flying clouds.

The intermittent light of the moon gave a magical, dream-like quality to their meeting. When they swam back to the yacht, and he said good night, he was in love.

If his father had not opposed the marriage, it would probably never have taken place. In the course of a normal engagement, he would surely have seen Margot for what she was. But Julian Vandenberg forbade his son point-blank to marry the girl, and so they eloped.

At first, it was all that he could hope for. His father cut off his allowance, but he had funds available and no scruple about spending them. He lavished presents on Margot, without heed as to what would happen when his limited cash ran out. He had never had to think of such problems. And Margot responded like a child—eager, delighted, incredibly loving. Strange as he was to women, Paul found himself in an entirely new world. His first innate shyness faded in the warmth of this red-haired girl's caresses, and he found new assurance in being her husband. His mother had died when he was in his teens, and since her death he had been a lonely boy. He never felt he knew his father. Julian Vandenberg was simply a remote, impressive, not particularly likeable man, who happened to have sired him. In a woman's company, therefore, Paul found a softness and a warmth that had been missing in the past few years.

But inevitably his money ran out. Afterwards he realized that Margot had gambled on Julian's relenting. It had not occurred to her that he would see his son go out to work as a clerk rather than countenance a marriage of which he disapproved. When Paul ceased to spend money on her, when bills began to pile up in the one-room apartment they had rented and Paul began to search for a job, the reality shocked her. To Paul it was an adventure. He would conquer the world as his father had done. He'd show him. What one Vandenberg had done, another could do. But that wasn't in Margot's plans.

To begin with, they simply quarrelled, squalidly and bitterly, over money. The first time it happened, it hurt, but Paul put the hurt away and made excuses for her. Then a new note crept into their bickering arguments. Margot began to taunt him with being a weakling, a mere boy, not man enough to stand up to his father. Paul did not answer her taunts. He met them with a tight-lipped silence that made her more furious than any reply could have done, and he gradually began to see another side to his beloved wife. Instead of a passionate, fiery lover, she became a vituperative shrew.

He found a job, concealing his parentage and trying desperately to look like a youth equipped for a future. It paid scarcely enough to meet the rent bill and keep them in groceries, but he felt proud and happy in it. Then he began to notice things about Margot. Although he could give her nothing, she still had money to buy little luxuries for herself. Never a good housekeeper, she became utterly slovenly about the apartment, and seemed never to be in it save on the weekends when he himself was there, and then she spent all her time lying on the couch, smoking. And when, finally, he challenged her about the money she was obviously spending, she was brutally laconic.

'If you can't make money, there are men who can,' she said off-handedly.

It was perhaps her complete indifference that shattered him. If she had pretended or lied to him it would have been easier to bear. But she simply looked at him coolly and smoked her inevitable cigarette and challenged him to do anything about it.

Their marriage lasted, after a fashion, for eight months after that. Before it ended, his father relented and offered to put Paul into one of his businesses, but Paul coldly refused. He was making headway in his job and, routine though it was, he was learning from it. Chiefly it was teaching him what the word independence meant, and he was enjoying the experience.

Those eight months left a mark upon him. At first, he could not believe that he had been so deceived about Margot. He tried to pretend to himself that it was the shock of their own poverty that had brought about the present state of affairs. But as though she delighted perversely in revealing herself to him now that there was nothing to be gained by playing a part, she began to tell him revoltingly intimate details of her former life. The yacht party at which he had met her was by no means her first; she was, in fact, very much in demand for such affairs, and she almost accused him of depreciating her value by marrying her under false pretences.

Through Margot, Paul learned a great deal about the hangers-on in his father's world. Her vicious, wounding confessions were a distorting mirror in which he began to see all the people who surrounded him. He saw even himself in the distorting mirror, like a grotesque creature at a carnival. He was the buffoon, the clown, the butt of the crowd, because he could not break with her.

That was the shameful thing. He began to hate her and to dread the moment when she looked at him, and smiled, and began to talk. Yet in spite of the loathing, he could not leave

[76]

her. He wanted her physically even while he despised both her and himself. Life with her was a constant degradation.

It was his father, finally, who put an end to it. He bought her off. The final ignominy for Paul was that she left him, and under such circumstances. When he knew that she had divorced him, it was as though a door had closed behind him and behind it, to be concealed for the rest of his life, were something shameful and humiliating. His father's interference widened the rift between them. Paul took ship as a steward on a small Dutch boat and vowed he would never see his father again.

As it happened, he did not. It was two years before Paul returned to the States, and when he did so it was in response to an urgent letter from his attorney. Julian Vandenberg had died of a heart attack on board his yacht, under circumstances peculiarly appropriate to his life, and his son was the sole heir to twenty million dollars.

The second image, hazy now with time even as it had been pale and self-effacing in their life together, was Lilian. What was the colour of her hair? Brown? He couldn't remember. She had had a fair, fine skin with a delicate colour—he remembered it was that air of fragility that first attracted him. She was a girl who had grown up in his own social group, the only daughter of a wealthy newspaper publisher.

They, too, met at a party, but it was a very different sort of affair. It was New Year's Eve, and he had been introduced to Lilian and then had forgotten her—that was the kind of girl that she was. But after Auld Lang Syne had been sung and most of the guests had gone home, he found her sitting, disconsolate, in a big easy chair before a dying fire. Her escort had disappeared without her (and no doubt with someone else) before the merriment had died, and she was trying to wait inconspicuously for all the company to depart before she called a cab. It seemed to him in that moment that something united the two of them. Paul had smiled at her, his gentle smile that was too old, too understanding for a man of twenty-four, and Lilian Harshaw, staring upwards through a mist of embarrassed tears, saw a slim, handsome, dark-haired young man who

B.M.—F

seemed to embody all she had ever dreamed of romance. From that moment she was his slave.

He took her home and they sat on the doorstep of her house and watched the sun rise and he told her why he had gone to the party, why he went to all parties, without a girl. The only thing that ever interested the girls he knew, he told her, was his money. It was a sad handicap and it made him very lonely at times. But he had got used to being lonely.

And she told him shyly, then, of her own loneliness.

'I know I'm not very pretty,' she said simply. 'Oh, don't misunderstand me—I don't really mind it. But . . . men don't notice me.'

And he didn't lie and tell her it wasn't so, because, sitting there on the step beside her while the sky turned from midnight blue to pearl-grey to pink, he could not remember the colour of her eyes.

After that, if he wanted a girl to take to a dance, it seemed natural to take Lilian. She was a restful, easy companion. Although shadowy, she was not a bore. He found it easy to talk to her, and in the glow of her adoration he expanded, gained new assurance. She helped smooth away some of the bitterness that Margot had left, she made supple the toughness that had grown in him during his two years aboard ship. As he began precociously to experiment with his father's businesses, she became his audience, his sounding board.

Six months after their first meeting, they were married. She was a lovely bride, pale and radiant, beautiful for the first and last time in her life. It seemed to their friends an ideal match. Lilian openly and ridiculously adored her husband, and if he found their marriage lacking in any particular he did not show it.

But for Paul it was the beginning of boredom. With Margot he had found at least the gratification of passion; even now he could recall the warmth of her body beside him and be hotly, pulsingly, agonizingly alive. With Lilian, there was nothing.

He had thought that she would bring him tenderness, comradeship, a gentle love that would be a background for his public life. But tenderness died in Lilian's fears, which he could not overcome. Comradeship fled when each looked at the

[78]

other, and knew: This is for life, this is for ever, and what have we? He learnt, too late, that tenderness which is not the afterglow of passion can be a withered branch.

They were married for two years. In all that time he longed fiercely for a child. When his desire was almost fulfilled, it was, ironically enough, Lilian who negated it.

She was a superb horsewoman. Their happiest time together was always the early morning, when they drove down to the riding club, picked out their favourite mounts, and went cantering through the morning mists. Paul had little enough enthusiasm for the sport, which had always frightened him, but because there were so few shared pursuits which brought the sparkle of happiness to Lilian's eyes he put aside his own reluctance and simulated a pleasure he could not feel.

Afterwards, he never knew whether she had not told him of her pregnancy because she was shy or because she did not want to miss those rides. But one sunny morning when the sky was a hot, bright blue, with swift-flying clouds racing across it, when the birds were singing with the ecstatic sweetness that belongs only to a June morning and the grass was diamond-dewed under their feet, the big grey that Lilian was riding shied at a frightened rabbit that shot between her hooves, and Lilian went over the grey's head.

The whole landscape tore apart just at that moment, rent by the mingled whinny of the horse and Lilian's scream. Then the birds were singing again and Lilian was staggering towards him, holding her stomach. And Lilian, immaculate, cool, grey-habited Lilian, was twisted in agony and red with her own life's blood.

She died in hospital, and his son or daughter (who knew which?) died with her. And even her dying was like her life: unmemorable, pointless. He found himself asking: Why? Why? And inevitably he blamed himself for not seeing what he should have seen.

And still, after all these years, he could not remember the colour of her eyes.

And then there was Louise. At twenty-eight, he thought he had found the ideal wife. She had the birth and breeding of his second wife, without her retiring shyness; she had beauty and vivacity equal to Margot's, but she was not a tramp.

By this time, Paul despaired of a marriage for love. There had been women in his life, aside from his marriages, but none had brought him happiness. Only for Margot had he felt a deep and consuming love, ironically enough. It seemed that the well-spring had dried up in him when she went out of his life. Perhaps he was too afraid of being cheated a second time to let himself go. However that might be, when he met Louise Carpenter in the home of a mutual friend in Boston, he felt: This woman will be my wife.

She was tall and dark, with sparkling brown eyes and a pert, tip-tilted nose that belied the dignity of her bearing. She was a brilliant conversationalist, with an air of warm sympathy that made her an enchanting dinner companion. She seemed fascinated by everything he did and said, yet there was a maturity and reserve about her that warned him she was not a woman given to adulation. And he felt reasonably sure that she was not interested in him for his money, but for himself.

In that, as in every other reaction he felt towards her, he was completely wrong. Louise Carpenter, at thirty, had one unsuccessful marriage behind her; her husband had died in an automobile accident, leaving her penniless. She had now one consuming ambition: to marry money. As a child she had not been poor, but she had not been rich, and her parents moved in a circle where money ranked second only to name. She had learnt early in life that the more elegant one's tastes, the more expensive they are to gratify. Even as a girl fresh from college, she had realized the necessity of making a successful marriage. Her one failure therefore rankled the more deeply, because it was a miscalculation. She had married a brilliant young man, a man with promise, and his sudden death and his lack of foresight in not providing himself with insurance had defeated her main objective.

When she met Paul Vandenburg, something kindled within her. She recognized opportunity. She also recognized the loneliness in his face, and she knew exactly how to present herself to him as the woman to overcome his loneliness.

For Paul, their marriage was a lesson in disenchantment.

At first, so skilful was her dissembling, he was not altogether aware of the reason for his sense of let-down. True, she was lacking in the physical warmth that he had hoped to find, but she concealed her frigidity so well that only a chance remark led him ultimately to recognize it. In the beginning, her beauty when he took her out and the admiring glances of his friends were sufficient to compensate for something that he sensed but could not define—a feeling that she was not really listening while she gazed at him with rapt attention and made the appropriate comments, a suspicion that she was not wholly absorbed in him when she kissed him, a small doubt that grew from her failure to remember any of their conversations or even keep straight in her mind his varied business activities.

Over the first few months of their marriage, the appalling truth drove in on him. He had married a colossal sham. Worse, she was a bore. Her poise, her charm, her warm sympathy—all were a careful pose, concealing—nothing.

When he finally reached this conclusion, his reaction was typical. He told her curtly that he wanted a son and had waited long enough. She answered as curtly that she had no intention of providing him with one.

It was only then that he realized to the full the reason for her elaborate pretence. In bitterness and recrimination the mask slipped. He saw, beneath, the hard, driving ambition, the determination to have money at all costs. Because he had always had it, money meant little to him, and he was surprised. But he recognized with fairness that Louise was out to make money in the only way she knew how, much as his father before him had been out to make money in the way he knew best. Marriage had once again proved to be an empty snare.

And then began the succession of women who held the night at bay for him. They had no meaning, save that they exorcized the devil of loneliness—at least temporarily. Many of the women learned to love him, but for none of them could he feel even tenderness. They served a purpose, that was all, and he was generous to them, and impersonal, and untouched.

It was a mere accident that gave him a son. Wryly, it amused him to think that the extremely efficient Louise could slip up in such an important particular. At first, disregarding her repugnance for the whole business, he began to concentrate his hopes for the future on the child, a boy, feeling that perhaps their empty union could now become warm and fruitful. But Louise did not take to motherhood any more naturally than to marriage. The youngster proved to be a sickly child, with a tendency to cry easily. In spite of his desire for a son, Paul Vandenberg found it difficult to love this small, peevish scrap of humanity.

The marriage rapidly degenerated. They were like two strangers living under one roof. Bored, lonely, and restless, Paul returned to the way of life that the birth of the baby had temporarily interrupted. He did not trouble to conceal from Louise the amours which occupied his leisure time. Furiously angry at his lack of discretion, which made her ridiculous in the eyes of her friends, she announced her intention to sue for divorce. Sardonically, he agreed immediately to her proposal, and the details were worked out with complete amity. For a very handsome consideration, she agreed that he should have custody of the boy.

Three wives. And what did they add up to now? A whore, a shadow, and a painted stage façade.

IX

A NAIL-ENAMEL test was in progress in the Interview Room. Six girls sat at the long table, hands spread flat before them, and when they were through six more would follow.

Lilian Verona applied nail enamel. From bottle Number One it went on to the thumb-nail, second and fourth finger-nails. From bottle Number Two she covered the remainder. It was a carefully worked-out system. For the next week, whatever they did, the girls on test would observe and report the condition of their finger-tips—wear, colour, lustre, any adverse reaction. And at the end of the week the test would be repeated, with another shade, from two further batches. The wear tests went on endlessly.

Paul Vandenberg entered, and stood unobtrusively near the door, watching the application. Not one of the girls was unaware of his presence. Even Lilian felt a slight tremor in her usually steady hands. She was Assistant to the Chief Chemist and was therefore frequently in contact with Vandenberg, but she had never overcome her initial shyness of him.

Vandenberg was tanned and rested. Two weeks in Florida's late spring sunshine had erased the signs of his recent attack. This was his first day back in the office, and he was anxious to return to work.

He moved over to the telephone and picked up the instrument.

'Tell the girls on special lipstick test to come into the Interview Room. Three at a time.'

Ziggie Anderson was in the second group. At first, he did not notice her. All the feminine employees, from his own secretary down, were rotated on these tests.

He stared intently at the lips of the girl before Ziggie.

'Any bleed?'

'No, sir.'

'Stay on when you eat?'

'Perfectly.'

'How about kissing?'

'Well—it smears a little.'

Ziggie was seized with a wild desire to laugh. Lipstick test always awoke her amusement, whether Vandenberg or (as was more usual) his Chief Chemist conducted it. They brought to it the gravity of high priests performing a religious rite.

Vandenberg was staring now at the girl's face. He did not look pleased.

'You're using far too much make-up. Take another training session with Miss Shepherd. Make-up is designed to enhance your features, not camouflage them.'

The girl he rebuked flushed scarlet, but said nothing.

'Next,' he said curtly.

Ziggie stepped forward, smiling.

'Hello, Mr. Vandenberg. How are you?'

One eyebrow was elevated slightly, then he recognized her.

'Oh—Miss Anderson. Fine, thank you.' He smiled perfunctorily, at the same time giving her lips the same intent examination he had bestowed on the preceding girls. 'Any bleed? Any smear?' And the inevitable: 'How is it when you kiss?'

It was obvious that he was interested in only one thing at this particular moment—the quality of the new lipstick.

It hurt her unaccountably. She should have known better, of course. He was Paul Vandenberg, head of a dozen enterprises. He didn't walk on the same level as his employees— save when he was drunk, perhaps.

He completed the routine questions and again said: 'Next.'

She resisted the impulse to shout at him: "To hell with your confounded lipsticks. Don't you ever see *people*?' and stalked back to her office.

It was only when Vandenberg was back in his own room that he thought about her. Then he realized: She asked me how I was. It wasn't just a routine question. I never even thanked her for what she did that night.

He reached out for his telephone, but at that moment it rang.

'Hello? Oh, all right. Bring them in. Yes, now. I'm free.'

Huberman, the head man of Merchandising, came in with the suggested shades for the Christmas promotion. He was a quiet, efficient-looking man who did not allow Vandenberg to push him around. He looked like a bank president or a stockbroker, and he was in fact a sculptor who had found the packaging and merchandising of cosmetics more lucrative than his chosen work. Only his wife knew what it cost him to live his Monday to Friday existence, and only his weekends in the studio, perhaps, enabled him to go on living it.

'Here they are, sir. All warm tones. Paris and the leading houses here are featuring green and russet-gold shades, so blue-reds are out. We've narrowed the choice to these five.'

Vandenberg stared at the swatches of material, the dabs of colour on the big piece of poster board. He shook his head.

'Orange is a hard colour. Doesn't suit many women, particularly in winter. Night light washes it out. I don't like these.'

'How about this one? Peachy, warm. . . .'

'Too pale. Only for the very young girl.'

'But the darker reds are too blue. They won't tone with green and rust. And a mid-red won't sit right with orange.'

'Why does a dark red have to be blue? Why not a dark scarlet?'

'Rather like saying a pale crimson, isn't it?'

'If we want it, we can have a pale crimson.'

Vandenberg rose and went over to a cabinet. Inside, on one neat shelf, were tubes of oil colours and a palette. He took up several tubes, made some dabs on the clean palette, studied the result, blended them with the brush. Then he returned to Austin Huberman.

'Something like that. Dark, almost maroon. But the yellow reds dominant.'

It was a rich, sombre splash of colour. Huberman stared at it doubtfully.

'I don't know. Dark shades have always been blue.'

'Why?'

'Perhaps because women like them that way.'

'Women like what you tell them to like. It may make most of them look like a bunch of corpses, but if you sell it, they'll wear it.'

He rang for his secretary. She entered immediately, a discreetly dressed, attractive but inconspicuous woman, probably in her late thirties.

'What do you think of that for a lipstick shade, Miss Shaw?'

She studied it, her head slightly tilted.

'It's gorgeous,' she said finally.

'Thank you, Miss Shaw.'

When she had left, Huberman remonstrated. 'She's not typical. Colour is her business. She *would* like it.'

What he meant was: She's your secretary. Do you expect her not to like your suggestion?

Vandenberg smiled. He understood perfectly.

'We'll get an impartial opinion,' he said suavely. He flipped the key on his intercom set. 'Miss Shaw, please get Miss Anderson in here.'

When she entered, her manner was as coldly impersonal as his own. He noticed it immediately, and smiled.

'Miss Anderson, first I must apologize. I was preoccupied with the test when I saw you outside. Thank you for your interest.'

She coloured. The sincerity of his manner and the gentle smile made her feel awkward as a schoolgirl. She caught the quizzical glance that Huberman threw her way.

'It . . . it's quite all right.'

She thought the words sounded ludicrously inadequate. Her heart was beating with unaccustomed violence and she knew that she had blushed.

She was grateful when he stopped looking at her and picked up the poster board.

'We are choosing a new shade, Miss Anderson. It has to be wearable with greens and orange-reds or gold. Now, we are having difficulty with the selection. We could have a pale shade, like these. Or we could have a deep, almost black shade —this. Still in the orange-red family.'

She compared them appraisingly, then picked up the palette. She rubbed her little finger in it, delicately, and smeared the smouldering, dark-toned pigments over her hand.

'I like this. The others are so ordinary. And orange lipsticks make the skin look yellow unless it's tanned.'

[86]

'Thank you, Miss Anderson. You've just chosen the Christmas shade.' He motioned her to a seat, then himself perched on the corner of his desk and turned back to Huberman. 'Have you or Helfer any ideas on a name?'

'We haven't worked on it yet. Had to peg the shade.'

'Hmmm. Something warm and exciting. Romantic. Miss Anderson, what does that suggest to you?'

'Sherry,' she answered promptly.

Huberman let out a guffaw of laughter. Vandenberg's eyes gleamed.

'How very appropriate.'

Again her cheeks burned. He noticed with amusement how easily she blushed. That fair, Scandinavian skin. It was rather beautiful. He found the delicacy of her make-up refreshing. It emphasized her youth, gave her an untouched quality.

'Maybe we should choose our names by a "word-association" method,' Huberman said dryly. He was annoyed.

Vandenberg was not listening.

'Sherry. And firelight. Or candlelight. Candlelight on the skin is gold. How about "Sherry and Candlelight"?'

' "Sherry by Candlelight",' Ziggie corrected, caught by the game. 'Sounds better. And it suggests more.'

'You wouldn't exactly drink sherry by candlelight—alone. You're right.' He was surprised and pleased. 'We can build a real promotion around that theme.' Again he flipped the key of his intercom set. 'Miss Shaw, find Mr. Helfer and get him in here. He is? Then get him on the 'phone.'

He paced up and down the carpeted floor—a vast amount of floor for an office. It was luxuriously appointed, with an eight-foot couch and heavy curtains that could be drawn to exclude the bustle of Fifth Avenue.

Ziggie, sitting in that office for the first time, was tense with excitement. She watched Vandenberg, knowing that he was now completely oblivious to her presence again.

She was amazed at the change in his appearance. He had lost the ghastly, almost transparent pallor and the heavy shadows that had darkened his eyes. He looked handsome and rejuvenated.

She was haunted by the thought of the brief period she had

[87]

spent in his apartment. She tried to put it out of her mind, but it kept recurring to her, and she found herself keyed up, excited, as though waiting on the threshold of adventure. She had thought about Vandenberg so constantly during the past weeks that it was a shock to her to realize that he was as much a stranger as before.

The telephone rang and he sprang to it.

'Oh, Murray, hello.' (He used first names only when he was particularly pleased about something. Otherwise his mode of address was formality itself.) 'I want you to work on the Christmas promotion. The name will be "Sherry by Candlelight", unless something much better comes up. Give it to the agency and let them work on it. Austin is with me—he'll check the copyright immediately. The colour is dark—dark and scarlet. Austin will get the lab working on it right away. Give it all you've got.'

When Austin Huberman left, Vandenberg indicated that she should remain. He was perched on the corner of his desk again, and he turned to her with a shrug and a wry smile.

'This is the part of the business that's fun. The beginning of a new promotion. After that, everything gets lost, and by the time we break I hate every shade and every name.'

It was a disarmingly ingenuous admission. She wondered: How could I ever have thought him cold? It is just that he is preoccupied, as he said. And so often, possibly, he feels ill.

He looked away from her, down at a paper-weight on his desk with which his fingers were playing.

'Miss Anderson. You were extremely kind . . . when I was sick. Thank you.'

She was at a loss for words. 'I did no more than anyone else would have done.'

'I'm not so sure.' He paused, still not looking at her. He seemed embarrassed. Then he said slowly: 'I realize I must have talked a great deal of nonsense. I hope you will—forget what you heard.'

For the second time, she felt wounded. So he was merely worried about any possible indiscretion. That was why he had kept her.

'You needn't be concerned, Mr. Vandenberg. I'm not in the habit of gossiping.'

He looked up quickly, noting the hurt in her voice. He felt inexcusably clumsy.

'I'm sure you're not. But—when one doesn't quite remember. . . .'

The telephone rang, and he swore.

'Hello? Yes, she's still with me. All right, all right. Here, wait a minute. . . .' He held out the receiver. 'Mr. Sarnoff wants you.'

Sarnoff was explosive. 'Where the hell do you think you are, Anderson? Do you work for Vandenberg or do you work for me?'

He was like an angry, jealous child. He wanted some papers which Woodstock could not find.

'I'll be right in,' she told him.

'Miss Anderson,' Vandenberg began, then stopped. 'All right. Get back to your office. But I want to see you before you leave tonight.'

However, at six o'clock he had not called her, and she was too proud to call him and invite a refusal.

As she locked up the office and turned out the lights before leaving, she thought: To hell with him.

X

THE late May sunshine streamed over the green lawn, glittering on the jewellery of the women, high-lighting the elegant white frame house. It was Sarnoff weather. All week the sky had been leaden and rain had fallen intermittently, but Sarnoff was giving a party and so the sun shone. Sarnoff had the luck.

It was an elegant party. In the main dining-room of the twelve-room Westchester mansion there was a buffet which would have fed the hungry of New York for a week—save that the richness of the delicacies would have turned any but an epicurean stomach. There was caviare to alternate with the more expected *gefüllte* fish—a concession to the taste of the special guest, The House of Vermeyer's President. There was champagne in buckets—imported, Harry would tell you, not any of this goddamned domestic crap. There was a hot buffet where one of the three coloured waiters, specially hired for the occasion, served sizzling hot hors-d'œuvres. And by way of entertainment there was a four-piece orchestra which played the latest numbers, substituting their own *risqué* lyrics as they moved among the guests, varying the boldness of their innuendo according to the particular group clustered around them. This was a special party. It was a party for Harry's daughter, Sarah, who was thirteen today. It was a great day. All of Harry's friends and business associates had to be there, all had to see the charm and grace of Sarah and the beauty of Harry's house, and go away shaking their heads, saying: 'Eh, that Harry . . . Did you ever taste such herring? Or the *gefüllte* fish. And the champagne—you'd think it was water, the way he pours it. Harry knows how to give a party.'

But Harry was wistful. He stood on the steps leading from the ornate playroom and stared down the half-acre garden at his guests, and he was not happy. Sarah was a good girl. She was smart, all right. But she was not a boy. Today should have been a *bar mitzvah*. Today he should have seen his son receiving the traditional gifts. It would have been a proud day then.

He watched Vandenberg. The slim, dark-haired man was on the lawn, mingling with Sarnoff's guests and making himself agreeable. It was an unwonted honour for Sarnoff that Vandenberg should have accepted his invitation. Harry knew his august boss avoided social engagements when he could. Well, his acceptance simply confirmed what his Vice-President already knew: Harry was special, and Vandenberg was smart enough to see that. Pride and satisfaction mingled with the sharp tang of regret as he watched his superior, and thought: Vandenberg has a son. He only has one child, but he has a son.

It was a strange thing, this desire for a boy, for flesh of your own flesh that was the same sex. It could never be the same with a girl, no matter how much you loved her. A girl could be a friend, but never the same close friend that a boy could be. There was always that barrier, that half-world of mystery that neither could cross. But a boy, now . . . You talked to him the way you would to your male friends. You taught him things. You shared in his life. You re-lived your own youth in his youth, you were with your first girl when *he* had his first girl. It was a dirty trick to play on a man like Harry not to give him a son.

'Hi-ya, Harry. Wunnerful party. Wunnerful.'

It was Steve Cates, one of their oldest salesmen, already staggering as he clung affectionately to Lilian Verona from the lab. Cates had been with them from way back, and he kept his job because he was still one of the smartest, but he liked his Manhattans too much. Before the party was over, a lot of the guests would be too full of Manhattans or Martinis or that eight-dollars-a-bottle champagne.

'Thanks, Steve. You're looking fine.'

'Never felt better. Feeling wunnerful. Weather's perfect, Harry. How you get such weather? All the lousy week it rains, then today it's wunnerful.'

'I give a party. The weather's always good when I give a party.'

'Good old Harry. Same old Harry. Always had the luck, any way you look at it.'

Harry grinned at Lilian, who was always a little scared of him, and showed it. 'Having fun, dollface?'

'Sure, Harry. Lovely party.'

Lilian worked for Marvin Stanbrook, the Chief Chemist, and Harry and Marvin were old rivals, so Lilian never liked to be too close to Harry. So now she smiled nervously and drew Cates away. Sure, Harry was a good guy, he gave a fine party and he was a good friend. But Marvin didn't like him, and Marvin was her boss.

Harry went back into the house to make sure all was going well there. Harry was a good host. He liked everyone to enjoy himself, and that meant that everyone must have plenty to eat and drink.

In the kitchen, Sally was busy checking last-minute, hot hors-d'œuvres which were ready to be taken out to the hot buffet. Those hot hors-d'œuvres always went faster than anything else. There were never enough. But she could always perform the small miracle of replenishment. Harry had to admit that no one could whip around the help and get things organized like Sally. She was happier in the kitchen bossing her help than she was out with the guests.

She flashed him a tentative smile, the nervous smile of a woman who is not as sure of herself as she tries to appear.

'Everything all right, dear?'

'Sure. Good party. You look nice, honey.'

'Thank you.'

She looked relieved. That was the funny thing about Sally. With the help she was a holy terror, yet with him she always seemed nervous, frightened.

She did look nice. She had good taste in clothes. But her simple black dress emphasized the thinness of her. He wondered why she had gotten so thin. When they were married she hadn't been that way. Now, in a low-cut black dress, you could see the sharpness of her bones. Her chest was hard and thin and she'd have been as flat as a board if she didn't wear falsies. That was something she never did when he married her, either. Well, maybe that's the way some women get when they have kids. Some get fat; others are like Sally, they get skinny.

'Come on, honey. Get out with the guests. It's okay in here.'

Sam and Ziggie were at the party. Harry liked to have his staff about him on such occasions. It made him feel good to introduce them to some of the doctors he worked with and his neighbours and his relatives. 'Jim, I want you to meet Miss Anderson, my secretary. And this is my assistant, Mr. Woodstock.' It gave him what he would call class. It wasn't every man who had a secretary *and* an assistant. And Ziggie was a special kind of girl. She wasn't like the rest of the bunch. There was about her what he would have called 'fineness'. The others felt it too, he knew that. Nobody ever told a really dirty story to Ziggie.

As Harry entered the living-room, he caught sight of Ziggie. She was sitting on a deep couch, talking to Sam and Dr. O'Malley. She too was wearing black. But on her it looked different. Harry stood still for a moment, unconsciously comparing her with his wife. Boy, that neckline really plunges. She isn't wearing a bra and on her it looks good. Ziggie, if you ever wear that dress in the office I'll take it off you.

At that moment, she stood up, and the dress fitted as he knew it would, smooth and sleekly tight over the hips, showing every line of her body.

'Don't go away, dollface. Here, have another champagne.'

He grabbed one from the tray of a passing waiter, and she took it, smiling at him.

'Many more and I'll fall flat on my face.'

'Not you, doll. You got a hollow leg.'

It was an old joke between them. He had often tried to get her drunk, but he had never succeeded. What he didn't know was that she fortified herself before one of his parties by drinking a glass of cream.

O'Malley toasted him. 'To the best host ever.'

The others joined in. Sarnoff's eyes crinkled.

'Thanks, kids.' His glance strayed around the room. 'Where's Gloria? Didn't she come?'

'Sure she came. She's out in the garden. She was talking to the big boss.'

Sarnoff looked sly. 'He seems to have taken a fancy to her.'

'She's looking great since her trip south. More like her old self than I've seen her look for months,' O'Malley said.

'That was P.V.'s idea. Figured it would set her up on her feet.'

Ziggie for once was less than warm.

'I don't know why he bothers. She'll fall off the wagon again.'

'That ain't nice, kid. She's had a rough break.'

'Plenty of people have rough breaks. The only way they get over them is by standing on their own two feet.'

'And the boss is helping her do that, Ziggie. He's a funny guy. If he drops you, he drops you, but if he thinks there's something to salvage he'll do more about it than most.'

'He's wasting his time. She hates him.'

'Doll, you just never liked Gloria.'

'That's right. I don't like someone who high-hats anyone that isn't a boss.'

Sarnoff grinned. Sure, none of the kids liked Gloria. She *did* high-hat them. She was grand. Gloria only knew people from junior executives up. But that was Gloria.

'Ziggie, you gotta understand. Gloria was somebody. She can't forget that. She was—well, like one of the movie queens. And she was just a kid.'

Sam felt that Ziggie was outnumbered.

'I can see what Ziggie means. I don't see where Gloria Vernon rates all the fuss. What does she do that's so special? Teach a few dumb manicurists how to apply nail enamel?'

Sarnoff lit up a cigar, and offered one to O'Malley.

'No, Sam, that's not the half of it. But you have to be part of the old gang to know what she meant. When Gloria came to us, she was just a leggy, eighteen-year-old kid. That was thirteen years ago. And we weren't such a hot outfit then, either. We were going places, but we still had to get there. Gloria worked hard. She came up with the company.

'Sam, do you remember what it was like in cosmetics twelve, thirteen years ago? Everybody but us had just one product— a lipstick, a colourless nail enamel, a face powder. It was kid stuff. No one was doing the whole works. But we were. We were starting it. That was Louis's big idea. Make a woman think of a lipstick as part of a wardrobe for her whole face and body. The works. It was a terrific idea. It was what made The House of Vermeyer. But Louis couldn't have put it across alone. There had to be a woman in on it—a show-case. And Gloria was it. Gloria *was* the Vermeyer girl. She went all over the country, she was photographed for every magazine, she was in short film ads in the local theatres. Stores featured the Vermeyer Salon Week—and Gloria was there to give the *spiel*. And she was gorgeous. A brain she might not have, but what she'd got was where it showed. Women wished they were like her. Men were crazy about her. And she just loved it. You bet she loved it. It was her whole life.'

'That and Louis,' said O'Malley.

'Yeah. She took that hard.'

'And you think Vandenberg wants to revive that business of—using her as a show-case?' Sam asked.

Sarnoff shrugged. 'No, I don't think so. She's too old for it now. Maybe he's just smart enough to know it's good business not to ditch a girl like Gloria. Or perhaps,' laying a finger along his nose and casting a sidelong glance at Ziggie, 'perhaps he—likes her a little bit. She's still a gorgeous gal.'

Ziggie rose to the bait. There was a hardness in her voice. 'I don't think P. V. would want someone else's leavings.'

'Ziggie, don't be a baby. P. V.'s old man died in the saddle, and P. V.'s his father's son. Don't you forget that.'

He grinned maliciously at Ziggie. So she is stuck on him, he thought. My little Ziggie. Jesus Christ, what's with the kid.

O'Malley looked thoughtful. 'You didn't invite Sadie.'

'No. You think I'm crazy?' Sarnoff let out a deep, throaty chuckle. 'Remember last time, Jim? Back in 'fifty-three?'

'Yeah. That was some party.'

'It was a *hell* of a party.'

'What happened?' Sam knew the question made him seem naïve, but he couldn't help it. This talk of old times made him feel raw and new, and he was sure Sarnoff meant him to feel that way. But he was interested.

'Sadie and Gloria really whooped it up. Sadie—that was Louis Vermeyer's wife—well, Sadie started it. It was really

[95]

funny, like something in the movies. Or it would have been, if it hadn't been so damn serious.'

O'Malley went off into a sudden spasm of laughter. 'I've never been able to eat borsch since. Not without seeing her.'

'It was an open-air party,' Sarnoff continued. He loved to hold forth to an audience, and the drinks were oiling his tongue. 'It was in June, and the weather was hot. Maybe that was why everybody got so worked up.'

'That and the Martinis,' O'Malley put in reminiscently. 'They were good Martinis. Gloria always went for them. That's what you've got to watch with Gloria. She's a dead sucker for a Martini.'

'And Sadie was drunk enough to be mean and not worry about looking ridiculous. She'd come with Louis, but of course he was with Gloria every minute he could get away from Jim and me.' Sarnoff was enjoying it all over again and Ziggie, watching him, remembered the whole episode, remembered it and felt disgusted with these two men who were re-hashing it and loving every minute of the recollection. 'She started by telling Louis to keep away from Gloria, and he told her she could go home if she didn't like it. And then she got mad, real mad. And she went after Gloria and told her right out in front of everybody to lay off her husband.'

'And Gloria picked up a bowl of borsch and poured it over her head,' said O'Malley, laughing excitedly, taking up the tale. 'Sam, you should have seen her. She's a homely woman, God help her, but you should have seen her then.'

'Her dress . . . Remember that lavender dress she was wearing?' Sarnoff slapped him on the back and laughed again. 'She was too fat for it, anyway, Sam, you got to remember that, and it was some thin stuff. The borsch soaked right through it and you could see her nipples. And then she bawled. Right there in front of us all she bawled, and she grabbed at Gloria and pulled at her hair, crying all the time, and the two of them had to be torn apart. . . .'

Ziggie was not laughing. Instead, she was watching Sarnoff coldly. Very quietly, she said to him:

'Sometimes I wonder why I work for you.'

He was still chuckling. He shrugged.

'So what's with you now?'

For a moment she did not answer. Then she tossed her head, as though to shake off the whole conversation. 'Good-bye. I'm off to find some more champagne.'

'Now how do you like that?' Sarnoff asked the world at large. 'What's eating her?'

'She doesn't like Gloria. Maybe she wished it was Sadie who poured the borsch.'

Sarnoff's eyes narrowed. He nudged O'Malley.

'No. Know what it was? I shouldn't of mentioned nipples. My secretary's real classy sometimes.'

And he nudged the doctor again and the two men roared with laughter.

The drinks are sure taking effect, Sam thought. Holy heaven, this could be a party. There's enough liquor to float a battleship, and everyone's half-canned already, and it's only four-thirty.

He excused himself and wandered off to find Ziggie. He felt like a fifth wheel around Sarnoff and his cronies. There were few people here he knew and even fewer he cared to know. But he was fascinated. What a bunch. What a crew. And this is one side of Vermeyers. Most of these people were the intimates of Louis, the founder of it all.

He found Ziggie standing under the trees, listening to the four-piece band. They were playing a catchy number that Sam did not recognize, with words that certainly would not have got by on television. At each punchline the cluster of people shrieked and howled with satisfaction. Except Ziggie. Sam, watching her, thought: She's completely out of place. She doesn't even look as though she's hearing it all. And then he saw what she was looking at.

Vandenberg was sitting at a small table that had been set, café-fashion, beneath the trees, a glass of what appeared to be lemonade before him, a mask of boredom on his face.

And Sam too knew: She's stuck on him. Poor silly kid. Stuck on sixty million and a legend, and he won't ever know she exists. That is, if she's lucky he won't know.

Vandenberg was not seeing the people around him or hearing the songs. He was unutterably bored. And when he was

[97]

bored his mind rescued him from his surroundings, took him to other places and problems. As he sipped his lemonade he was thinking of a company that he could acquire, if he wanted to. And the problem he was turning over in his mind was: Should I? What pleasure will it bring me? Why bother? Why not simply take a rest, go away from all this and all the other companies?

But rests irritated him; he was too active. And a change of scene was merely the exchanging of one pattern of boredom for another. He wondered whether he should take Laurie to Europe. But he feared that several weeks of each other's company might prove insupportable to both of them. The boy was afraid of his father. That was the one thing Vandenberg could not overlook. They might have nothing in common, the boy might be hostile, that he could forgive; what he could not bear to look upon was the nervousness in his son's face on the rare occasions when they spent any time together.

He came abruptly out of his reverie as he was joined by someone. It was Gloria Vernon. He had spoken to her earlier, quite briefly. It had amused him to note that she was even more antagonistic towards him now than she had been before. So he glanced across at her in some surprise.

'Mr. Vandenberg . . . You don't mind if I join you?'

'Quite the contrary. I'm delighted.'

'I—wanted to thank you. I should have done so before.'

There was still an air of mingled embarrassment and hostility in her manner, in spite of the words. He half-smiled. She really doesn't like me. And it kills her to have to be grateful to me for something.

'Miss Vernon, you don't have to thank me. You have more than earned an extended vacation by your past service to the company.'

'I'm fully aware that that wasn't why you sent me away.'

He shrugged. 'Why think about it? I hope you had fun.'

She was not yielding. He noticed the nervous movements of her hands and the way her glance followed the waiters who passed them with trays of varied drinks.

'Not particularly. I know that's very ungrateful of me.'

'But natural. I never have fun myself when I take a trip. It's usually on my doctor's orders and it isn't amusing.'

Her eye caught his glass. 'You're not drinking, either.'

'No. Sometimes I do, but I always wish afterwards I hadn't. The pleasure of drinking is hardly worth the price my ulcer makes me pay for it.'

She stared at him with genuine interest, for the first time.

'That's funny.'

'What is?'

'The fact that you can't drink. People always think of someone like you as having—the whole world. And you can't drink.'

It seemed to him that she rather enjoyed the fact.

'The world is a big word. I have only money.'

'Only. . . .' She gave a bitter little laugh.

'You think it's so important?'

'The only people who don't think it important are those who have it. And they don't know what it's like to be without it.'

'Have you been poor, Miss Vernon?'

'Oh yes. I was born poor. My family were good people, but they were poor. They brought me up to do all the right things, and not envy those who had more than I had. To go to Mass and be modest. Big joke, isn't it?'

'I don't see anything humorous in it,' he said quietly.

'That's very nice of you, Mr. Vandenberg. Considering I know—what everyone says about me.'

For a moment he did not say anything, but studied her face. Then he said abruptly:

'The chief thing that's wrong with you is that you think too much about yourself. You take out what you consider to be your sin and paw over it, like a miser with a bag of gold.'

She flushed. 'That's—not a very nice thing to say.'

'I'm not a very nice person. Did I pretend to be?'

She was at a loss for words. She glanced at him angrily, then her eye was caught by a waiter who was passing down the garden near their table. She called to him.

'Waiter—I'll take a Martini.'

The boy placed one on the table before her, then turned to Vandenberg.

'For you, sir?'

'No, thank you.' He motioned him away, and turned back to Gloria Vernon with a somewhat wry smile. 'So now you are going to get drunk because I was unkind to you.'

'It's my own business, I think, if I have a drink. I'm not on company time.'

'Oh, yes, it's your own business. Just a pity, that's all.'

'I suppose you are going to tell me you hate to see a woman drunk.'

'No. In point of fact I don't care to see anyone drunk, man or woman. None of us do. Particularly when we know we look the same way ourselves.'

She drank greedily and steadily. It was not the way a person drank who liked the taste of the liquor. She drank because she had to be drunk. He knew women like that. As the false fire went down, she would begin to sparkle. She would be good company at first. Then she would go just that little bit over, the exhilaration would go and depression would seize her. She probably cried when she was drunk.

What the hell, he thought. We all cry, if we're unhappy. In a man it takes a different form. He goes out and gets a woman, spends himself that way.

'Tell me about yourself,' he said to her.

'What is there to tell? The same old story.'

'To me it will be new.'

'My folks were Irish. Poor Irish. I never had pretty clothes when I was a kid. I went to a Catholic school and I went to church regularly, and I looked at the girls who had pretty clothes and wanted to be like them.'

She had almost finished her drink. She eyed it with absorption, then glanced around. She didn't want to finish it until she knew she could get another. That was the bad thing about taking a drink. It couldn't be one. For some people, one drink was enough. Or two. They could stop. They didn't know how lucky they were. Oh God, if she could stop, once she had started. Now she was sitting here with Vandenberg's dark eyes watching her, getting pie-eyed. Even now, while she was still sober enough, she knew she would get pie-eyed. And he'd probably can her. Oh, what the hell.

He noticed how her eyes clouded. The bright, clear blue seemed to blur. They were Irish eyes, as he now realized, set far apart, with thick black smudgy lashes that owed little to mascara. She was not a type of woman that attracted him, but he could see how she might have been quite devastating as a youngster. And he thought back to that, as she talked. He thought of the way she must have been when she met Louis Vermeyer for the first time. He would have had an easy game with a girl like Gloria.

'Vermeyers was almost my first job,' she went on. She had caught the eye of the waiter now and he was bringing her another drink. She wondered if Vandenberg would stop her, but he made no move. 'I was eighteen when I came here. I did everything—manicurist, receptionist, travelling salesgirl—we used to call them salesgirls then, not consultants. I loved it. I went all over the place. At first I earned thirty-five dollars a week. I thought it was a fortune. I'd never been so well off.'

'And then you found—it went.'

'Yes. That was the funny thing. It was so much at first, and then it wasn't enough. And I got a raise. And still it wasn't enough. And I wanted so much to get on. I worked hard. I worked darned hard. And finally I began to make the grade.'

He was thinking back. The most satsifying money he had ever made had been the twelve dollars a week that he earned when he was first married. Everything else about that time had faded now, or almost faded, but he remembered that. It had given him a sense of achievement. It had almost made him feel free of his father.

The way our parents affect us, he thought. Gloria now is unhappy mostly because she has let them down, those good, poor, God-fearing people. I wonder if she abandoned them on the way up. And I—I am ashamed of my own talent for making money, because my father made money and tainted it for ever. How quaint we are.

He knew that if he went on sitting there, listening to her, she would get plastered. She would probably get plastered anyway, but at least he need not be there to witness it. He was surprised himself to find how much he pitied her.

He rose.

'If you will excuse me. I have to find Mr. Sarnoff.'

She nodded, relieved. 'Of course.'

As he went from her, up the sloping lawn to the house, again the pain of remembrance filled her. The build—it's the same. It might be Louis. Damn his eyes, it might be Louis alive again.

But Louis had never spoken to her as this man spoke to her. He had never seen into her, the way this man made her feel he saw into her. That was what made her talk to him. Hell, why had she told him that about her parents? What business was it of his?

Angrily, she finished her drink, and waved to a waiter for another.

Sarnoff was in the midst of a group of cronies in the living-room, as Vandenberg entered. He was selling them something, and Vandenberg caught the end of his harangue.

'I tell you, Austin, you can't lose. For a hundred dollars you get one chance in a hundred. And it's tax deductible. It's a charity. In your bracket, Austin, you can't lose.'

Austin Huberman grudgingly took out his cheque-book. Whatever it was he was buying, it was obvious he did not need it. Sarnoff was grinning like a fat cat. Then he saw Vandenberg.

'Hey, boss. I'll cut you in on this. I just got two tickets left.'

'Tickets?'

'For the raffle. For a Cadillac. For a hundred dollars you get one chance in a hundred to win a brand new, super de luxe Cadillac.'

'I have two,' Vandenberg observed dryly, yet enjoying the sheer effrontery of the man. No one ever tried to sell Vandenberg anything.

'Okay. So you don't need it. It's a charity. It's for my Temple. And you deduct it from your income tax.'

It was the old game, of course. It was the game all these men played. You give to my charity and I'll give to your charity. But Vandenberg was above it. Head and shoulders above it. It amused him that Sarnoff had the nerve. He liked that.

He took out his cheque-book and wrote out the cheque.

'Aren't you afraid it might cost you more than a hundred to have me buy a ticket from you?'

Sarnoff grinned again.

'No, boss. Of you I ain't afraid.'

As Vandenberg left the party, shortly afterwards, he was still trying to decide how to take that remark. And it was not often that anyone left him guessing.

SHARON ROBERTS, emerging with an effort from her own preoccupations, watched her room-mate. Ziggie had washed her hair and was sitting on the floor wearing a terrycloth robe, propped against the leg of a couch. She was mending a pile of underclothes, with steady deliberation.

At one time, Sharon would have noticed nothing. But now she recognized a new reserve about Ziggie, and she knew what it meant. Ziggie was hiding something, because it hurt.

She spoke gently.

'All right. Give.'

Ziggie looked up. '*Comment?*'

(A lot of her college crowd thought it smart to smatter a few easy French words into their conversation. Normally Ziggie was not one of them, and the forced brittleness was duly noted by Sharon.)

'I mean give. When a girl tackles a pile of torn shoulder-straps and missing buttons that have been accumulating for more than a year, it means only one thing.'

'All right, wise one. What does it mean?'

'That she wants to be occupied. When you're occupied you don't have to talk.'

'Don't be ridiculous.'

If there had been nothing on her mind, she would have looked up at Sharon with her wide, candid gaze, and laughed the notion off. Seeing her glance still averted, Sharon knew she was right.

They were, in an undemonstrative way, exceptionally fond of each other. They had met during Sigrid's first year in New York. The latter was then living in a tiny, one-room apartment in the East Eighties, and typically, having cleared the first hurdle of leaving her parents' home and achieving independence in New York, Ziggie had decided that she could and should do better in the matter of accommodation. So she advertised for a girl to share an apartment. Sharon was one of those who responded. She was twenty-two, a born New Yorker, worldly-wise and cynical but with an easygoing temperament that made her an ideal companion for the more volatile Ziggie. What had started out to be a mere economic arrangement became the beginning of a genuine friendship.

So now Sharon waited for a moment, then said with deceptive mildness:

'I would say that you had a problem. And I would further say that it had to be a man.'

Sigrid's face was still non-committal. She answered shortly.

'Since you know so much, tell me more.'

'I'd say it was . . . Sam Woodstock.'

Ziggie did look up at that, and laughed explosively.

'Sam. . . . Oh, no. No, my dear, not Sam.'

Sharon's composure was not ruffled. She was still watching her room-mate with apparent casualness.

'Then the man is wrong. But there *is* a man. There has to be.' Then she added, as though it were an after-thought: 'And I don't know why you laugh. Sam's a nice guy.'

Ziggie was glad to pursue this side issue.

'He's very sweet. Perhaps that's what's wrong with him.'

'You're not making sense.'

'Yes, I am. He bores me. I always know what he is going to say and do, because it will be the right thing.'

'Every young man you meet bores you.'

'So perhaps I don't like young men.'

'Hogwash, my dear.'

There was silence for perhaps five minutes. Then Ziggie spoke, musingly.

'Sharon.'

'Ummmm?'

'What do *you* want? I mean, in the way of a man.'

'I don't know. Any nice young man, I suppose. Just so he's my type of man.'

'But that's what I mean. What *is* your type of man?'

It was Sharon's turn to pause. She was lying sprawled in an easy chair, a book on her lap. Now she fingered the leaves, absently. Her face, when she was not animated with conversation, was serious, almost sad. Ziggie noticed, not for the first time, the new tension about her mouth. It was a strong, resigned face, not a happy one.

She answered slowly.

'I suppose—someone like Jerry. If only he would have stayed put. He was so darned sweet, and fun, too. But . . . a girl has to have security, something to hang on to. With him I would have had nothing. For him—there was always something over the next hill. He'd never stay put long enough to make any money.'

'Do you think—maybe you should have married him? Even without the security?'

'Good Lord, no. What sense would there have been to that? I'm used to certain things, let's face it. I can always make my own living. I couldn't just marry him and tag along—wherever the fit took him. Never getting anywhere. You can't live on love.'

That was a familiar note. Yes, that was what she had been taught all her life, Ziggie thought. Her mother had always told her: 'You don't have to marry for money, dear, but you do have to have something. What you're used to. When you're broke, love dies awful fast.'

Her mother. Sigrid Anderson would have told you that she was very fond of both her parents, but at such moments as the present she realized she had very little in common with them. Perhaps that was why she had had to leave home. She couldn't fit into their pattern of life.

Not that she had ever quarrelled with their attitude, until now. But she looked at Sharon, saw the changes in her face since she had broken up with Jerry, and wondered.

'You know,' she said slowly, 'when you used to come home after being out with Jerry, you looked so different. It was as though—someone had lit candles in your eyes.'

'Ziggie. . . . Please.'

'I know. I'm being cruel. Well, what the hell? You're right. We try not to talk about things, because they hurt.'

'Talking doesn't do any good, I suppose. Anyway, what has this to do with—whatever is on your mind?'

'I don't know. I really don't know. I don't even know what *is* on my mind. I'm not in love. At least, I don't think I am. Maybe that's the trouble.'

'You just want to be in love, so that you too can feel miserable and romantic.'

'Don't laugh, Sharon. It's not that childish. I feel—restless. Maybe Sam does have something to do with it. I'm not in the least interested in him, but I think he is in me. And to me he's just impossible. Completely impossible.'

Sharon was thinking: She's such a child in some ways, even though she's twenty-six. And in others—so too-too smart. But she simply asked:

'Why?'

'Maybe it's the way we're brought up. Mother would die if I married him. And I—I can't picture it. He'd always be poor —he has a crowd of relatives sponging on him. And he likes to go to Europe each year, even though it keeps him broke.'

'He sounds like Jerry.'

'Yes. Only he doesn't matter to me. If he did—it would be horrible. Sharon—why are we so damned materialistic?'

'My dear, I don't see it as materialism. A woman has to be practical. If you can make a good living for yourself, why should you take anything less, just by getting married?'

'But if that's all there is. . . . If you can't have your cake and marriage too—what do you do?'

Sharon fought down some stubborn echo that said, Yes, what do you do? What does it feel like now, without Jerry? But she said simply:

'I don't see why one need be so desperate about it. There isn't that urgency. You just—wait.'

Ziggie did not reply at first, then said with seeming irrelevance:

'You know, at the party, I was watching Gloria Vernon. She got drunk again, of course. I knew she'd fall off the wagon. And she looked awful. But I couldn't help remembering—the way she looked when Louis Vermeyer was alive.'

Sharon stared watchfully. This apparent non sequitur threw her.

'What has that to do with you and Sam?'

'Nothing. Not with Sam. Just with—me. Sharon, Gloria's a career girl. She got pretty high up the ladder. She—had it made, as they say in Vermeyers. And now look at her.'

'That's different, Ziggie. You know what makes her that way.'

'It's not different. I keep asking myself: What happens next? I'm twenty-six, I've got a good job, I think I'm pretty smart. And then, suddenly, I begin adding it all up, and it doesn't seem to amount to much. I'm not married. I'm not in sight of marriage, and yet I want children. I want them desperately.'

She was wound up now. She had put down her mending and was staring ahead of her, unseeingly.

I wish I were like my grandmother Sigrid, she thought. She came to a new country when she was eighteen. And even New York wasn't enough for her. She wanted it—all new. She went west. She found a man. She didn't worry whether he was social register or whether he had enough money. Life was simpler then. Now—it doesn't play fair.

Sharon did not know what it was all about, but she let her talk.

'Sharon—all our lives we're brought up to think certain things, to want certain things. Whenever I've thought of men, of a husband, I've thought of a ring. I've thought of a big wedding, and me in a beautiful dress, and presents, and Mother crying and yet being happy and loving it all. And Dad giving me away, and feeling very proud because his little girl was getting married. And after the wedding I could picture the house we would live in and the friends we would have and our first car. And it would all be very comfortable and secure and *right*.'

She paused. She seemed to expect an answer. Sharon said slowly:

'Well, what's wrong with all that?'

'You don't see anything wrong with it?'

'No.'

'There's one thing left out, Sharon. The man. I never could picture the man. He—he didn't seem important. It was all the other things that seemed important.'

Her face was very tense and her hands clasped a torn slip.

[108]

Sharon was startled. She did not know Sigrid in this mood. She asked with sudden urgency:

'Ziggie—what's happened? What are you so het up about? Why are you talking about Gloria Vernon?'

'Nothing's happened. That's what's so—terrible. I've met someone who changes everything, and he doesn't even know I exist. Oh, I'm not in love with him—I'm sure of that. But —when I look at him, I feel—excited. I like to look at him when he's not looking at me. And when he does look at me, I think I know—what it would be like to be in bed with him. And I—want that.'

Her voice had sunk to a whisper, and she turned her face away, so that Sharon could not see it. For a while there was silence, then Sharon laughed a funny, unhappy little laugh.

'I felt that way—about Jerry. I never told you.'

'But you didn't.'

'No. It would have been wrong.'

'Why, Sharon? Why, if you felt that way only for him?'

'Because—because we weren't married. You can't do these things. It cheapens you.'

'It lowers our value in the marriage market, you mean.'

'No, that's not what I mean. That's—well, it's a trite and melodramatic thing to say.'

'If you'd gone to bed with Jerry, you might have decided to marry him, even without security.'

'Well, I didn't, and I wouldn't, and I'm glad.' She spoke vehemently, because of the spectre Ziggie had recalled. 'And anyway—what *is* all this about?'

'I don't know. Yes, I do. Suddenly, I'm looking ahead to a long procession of young men who mean nothing, who do nothing to me, young men I could marry. I know that I've never felt anything or been anything before. I've not been a woman. Now—now I think I know what it feels like, to be a woman.'

'But Ziggie . . . Why does it have to be so desperate? Why should it be so one-sided, this feeling of yours?'

Ziggie picked up her mending again and methodically sewed on a button.

'Because . . . it's Paul Vandenberg.' And again she said,

almost inaudibly: 'And he doesn't even know I exist. Not even when he talks to me.'

Sharon felt as though something had hit her. She stared at Ziggie unbelievingly.

'Ziggie. . . . He must be years older than you. And he'd never marry you.'

Ziggie smiled helplessly. 'I know. That's what I mean. And you sound just like Mother.'

Suddenly, she put her face down in her hands. Sharon wondered if she were crying.

Oh no, she's not in love, she thought. Not a bit of it. Damn Vandenberg to hell.

XII

SARNOFF leaned back in his chair.

'Okay, Sam. Let's make sure we've got everything. You got the number of cases?'

'Yes, sir.'

'Breakdown—consumers, salons, and doctors' offices?'

'Yes, sir.'

'And the total sales figures?'

'All here.'

Sam knew that this was a game. Sarnoff did not need him to provide the figures. But he was to participate in a top-level conference. He felt vaguely uneasy. He suspected that Sarnoff's aim was to discredit him in the eyes of P. V.

Sam had very few illusions. In spite of the lack of contact with the President, he suspected that he had been hired to act as a combined back-stop and investigator in the office of the Vice-President. Pollovic, the Director of Personnel, had hinted as much. But in both capacities Sam felt that he had failed dismally. He found out only what he was meant to find out. Sarnoff and Ziggie were a team—a very close-working, harmonious team. Sarnoff did not even give him any work to do and, because of the unaccustomed idleness, on the very rare occasions when he was called upon to do something he did it badly. He had become over-anxious. Sarnoff from the beginning had been cagey with him; now his initial mood of caution had gone and he treated his new assistant with thinly disguised contempt. Because Sarnoff acted as though he were stupid, Sam found himself, for the first time in his life, behaving as though he were stupid. He was losing his self-confidence.

So he was uneasy. He had taken this post in good faith, and given up a promising legal practice to do so. He had thought to act as bona fide House Counsel. Instead, his most important duty was acting as errand boy for Sarnoff. ('Hey, Sam, I left my car at the hotel. Park it for me, that's a good boy. . . . Sam,

I'm going up to the Concord for a day or two. Need a rest. Yeah, yeah, I been overdoing it. I'd like you to drive me. . . . Sam, there's a package there. I'd like you to put it in the back of the car. No, not that one, stoopid, the big one. Give the doorman a dollar. . . .')

No, this was not much of a job for the bright young man voted 'most likely to succeed' of his class at N.Y.U. But then, Sam reflected, none of this business was standard. It was all too easy. You bottled and canned a few products, sold them under fancy names with fancy claims, and the dollars rolled in. He still didn't get it.

And when he remonstrated with Sarnoff that he wasn't doing enough, that he wasn't being used for legal work, Sarnoff simply answered off-handedly: 'Wait. You'll earn your keep. Don't worry about it.' With that he had to be content.

Sarnoff was looking at his assistant now, his expression sly.

'Know what I'm going to recommend?' (He was aware that Woodstock knew exactly what he was going to recommend, since he himself had told him. But he was talking merely for effect, as they both knew.) 'Pull the product. Only thing. Pull the product.'

'But I don't see how we can. Or why we should. We don't *know* it's the fault of Youth Elixir.'

'Sam. We got over two hundred and fifty cases. It couldn't just be a coincidence.'

Sam was about to dispute the point when Ziggie's buzzer sounded. It caught him with his mouth open, and there was nothing for him to do but close it again, feeling foolish. He always argued with Harry. He didn't know why, except that with so little else to do there seemed an imperative need to justify his existence somehow, and so he argued. It did not annoy Sarnoff. If anything, it pleased him, because Sam was usually wrong. And Sam was aware of that fact.

'Okay, doll.' Sarnoff got to his feet eagerly. 'Come on, Sam. He's ready.'

Sarnoff led the way to Vandenberg's office with a light, springy step. Such sessions were meat and drink to him. Not that he wanted trouble for The House of Vermeyer, of course, but when that stupid sonofabitching chemicker got them into trouble it was always Sarnoff's job to get them out of it. And that was what kept his value up.

Stanbrook, the Chief Chemist, was already with Vandenberg when they arrived. So was Austin Huberman. It was obviously to be a very private conference, with Sales and Publicity not represented.

Vandenberg came straight to the point.

'We don't have to waste time, Stanbrook. I've told you briefly the problem as I have it from Harry. STX-3, the operative ingredient in Youth Elixir, is undoubtedly a wonder ingredient. It appears to do all we claim for it. However, it also appears from the complaints we have received that it stimulates the growth of hair.'

'I don't believe it, sir. We tested it.'

Stanbrook was smiling. He was a small, dark-haired man with a blandly youthful face. His easy-going air was at once a hall-mark and a disguise. No one ever saw Marvin Stanbrook ruffled. He, with Sarnoff, completed the original triumvirate which had created The House of Vermeyer. Vermeyer had the brain, Stanbrook the knowledge of chemistry, and Sarnoff the strong right arm. . . . These were the original ingredients of the success formula.

Vandenberg, who had gone into the history of Vermeyers very thoroughly before he moved in, knew all this. He valued Stanbrook at exactly the appropriate evaluation. Which was to say that he trusted him as much as he would have trusted a convicted forger.

'I know you tested it,' he said gently. 'We're not trying to find any negligence. It just happens that no test could be comprehensive enough to pinpoint this sort of result.'

'What have we got? A few crank letters.'

Sarnoff shook his head. He was sitting well forward in his chair, his eyes bright. He said softly:

'Not a few, Stan. And not crank. Some of them have medical reports. The women have been to doctors, and the doctors have certified that Youth Elixir grows hair.'

Between Sarnoff and Stanbrook had always existed a bitter rivalry. Both had acknowledged the superior talents of

[113]

Vermeyer, but neither could concede that the other lieutenant was necessary. Vandenberg, assessing them, knew that success would have been impossible without them both; he was also increasingly of the opinion that continued success would be impossible without the removal of at least one.

'How many letters have you received, Harry?'

(Sarnoff liked that; the boss called him by his first name, but not the others.)

'Two hundred and fifty-three, boss. In the first two months. They were all received in the second month.'

Stanbrook moved irritably, still smiling. 'Two hundred and fifty-three. Do you know how many bottles were sold in the first month?'

'Yes, Stan. One million, three hundred—what was it, Sam?'

'One million, three hundred and twenty-one thousand, two hundred and thirteen bottles,' read Sam from his notes.

'Okay. And the second month will run nearly as high.' Stanbrook was returning to the charge. 'So you have approximately one complaint for every ten thousand users.'

'It's too much, Stan. And that ain't all. I got doctors. And they have cases. Bad cases. They don't like this product. And you know what happens, Stan, if the doctors don't like our products.'

Harry was playing his trump card, and he knew it. Even Stanbrook didn't like that ugly word 'doctors'. Because the dermatologists could really hit you. Boy, if they said a product was no good, that product might just as well have been no good. Because they killed it dead.

All his business life Harry had had the doctors on his side. He had been smart. He had seen, right at the beginning, that when you put something on a woman's skin you'd better be careful. Maybe she'd be allergic to it. Maybe she'd come up in a rash or get her eyes puffed up or lose her finger-nails. Skin was funny. Skin was living. Made the beauty business like the medical business. Things could go wrong. So better have the doctors on your side, then when something went wrong they worked for you, not against you. Get the woman into a smart doctor's office, pay her medical bills, make her feel she was important, special, unusual—the one in fifteen thousand who couldn't use a tested product. Every woman fell for that. Every woman liked to feel she was unique.

Huberman cleared his throat.

'So what are you recommending, Harry?'

'I'm recommending that we pull the product off the market, Austin. We can't afford this kinda trouble.'

'Do you think we can afford to pull it?'

'We have to. We don't have no choice.'

'You're forgetting one thing, Harry. You're only seeing one side of it—and you're right, I'm not quarrelling with your view of the seriousness of the problem. But Youth Elixir had a tremendous publicity campaign. It was promoted in newspapers, magazines, on radio and T.V. It's selling like mad, and women love it. If we pull it, everyone will know that something is wrong with it. Something bad. Even the women who didn't grow hair on their face will wonder what *was* wrong. Even we can't afford that sort of withdrawal. It will shatter public confidence in our entire line.'

Sam was fascinated. He stared from one absorbed face to the other and tried to take this thing seriously. As an attorney, he could see the implications, all right. When a woman grows hair on her face, boy, you've got trouble, because you're hitting her where she feels it most—in her vanity. But it still seemed to him an incredibly magnified problem. He looked at Vandenberg, watching intently one speaker after another, and thought: He can't take it this seriously. Pull the product off the market and have done with it. We'll survive. This is Vermeyers. This is the biggest of them all.

Stanbrook was talking again.

'Austin's right. And I still think we're getting worried too easily. We've had things like this before. We've survived them. And never before have we had anything so revolutionary as this cream. My wife uses it. She looks literally ten years younger. And she hasn't grown hair!'

'Stan. I don't listen to the women who like it,' Harry explained patiently, as though to a child. 'I listen to the doctors. And just because your wife don't grow hair doesn't mean that the girl down the street who keeps a little millinery store won't grow hair. Because her skin's different, her body's different, she reacts in a different kind of way.'

'Harry.' Stanbrook adopted the same tone of patient resignation. 'Did you ever hear of a sulpha reaction?'

'Yes. I heard of a sulpha reaction. And a penicillin reaction. So what does that prove? Don't give me no crap, Stan. These are drugs. You gotta take chances with drugs, because otherwise the patient might die. But we ain't selling drugs, Stan, we're selling cosmetics. And I say we gotta product here we shouldn't be selling. I said it before, I still say it. It can get us in trouble.'

'With one in ten thousand. And the other nine thousand, nine hundred and ninety-nine will be delighted.'

Vandenberg had followed the discussion with unmoved features. Now he said, his voice almost bored:

'You're missing the point, Stanbrook. It's not how many that counts. All right, you have only two or three hundred women who have written in so far. But they are two or three hundred women with hairy faces. Can you imagine what your own wife would feel like, Stanbrook, if she suddenly grew a beard? Or what you would feel like? This growth may be irreversible. What will she do—use a razor? Live at an electrolysis office? Can you imagine what *that* would do to our line?'

Huberman was silent. Stanbrook, not yet ready to concede, said suddenly:

'Let's see the letters.'

Vandenberg turned to Sarnoff. 'Got them with you?'

Before Sarnoff could ask him, Sam put in:

'They're in the office.'

Sarnoff pursed his lips. Vandenberg flipped the intercom key.

'Ask Miss Anderson to bring in all letters on Youth Elixir.'

They waited, gloomily. Sam was cursing himself for not bringing the case files. He should have anticipated that.

There was a knock at the door and Ziggie entered, a pile of thin folders in her arms. She brought them over to Vandenberg's desk. They were separated into three groups. She indicated the first.

'These are probably unimportant. Either exaggerated, or very doubtful. This second batch are serious, but without medical reports. In all these,' and she indicated the third and largest group, 'the woman has been to a doctor. You need only read a few from each group, I think. They are all fairly typical.'

'Thank you.' He was not looking at the files, but at her hands. They were exceptionally beautiful, and faultlessly manicured. Almost automatically, he took hold of one, examining it professionally. 'You do your own nails?'

'Yes, sir.'

'You do a nice job.'

Stanbrook grinned. 'Wish she were as good with her face.'

Vandenberg looked up, surprised. 'What's wrong with it?'

'Look at it. Practically no eye make-up. She doesn't use the standard application methods. And she won't co-operate on tests.'

Before Vandenberg could speak, she replied for herself.

'I make my face up as I see fit. And I test everything except creams. I prefer soap and water.'

'You're unco-operative, dear,' Stanbrook smiled at her. 'Be careful.'

'Are you *threatening* her, Stanbrook?' Sarnoff's voice was explosive. 'Quit picking on my girl! What kind of a man are you, to pick on a girl? She does a good job. If you had one man in your crappy department that did as good, maybe we wouldn't have so damn much trouble!'

Stanbrook was about to speak, but Vandenberg cut in icily.

'Are we discussing Youth Elixir? Or Miss Anderson's face?' To Ziggie, he added: 'Thank you. That's all we need.'

He noticed approvingly the stubborn set of her chin as she withdrew silently. She wouldn't be pushed around. That was good. A man who could be pushed around wasn't worth his first day's pay.

He turned to the files. There was silence as he read. At one point he muttered: 'Good God.' Austin watched him, while Stanbrook looked at the floor, and Sarnoff, grimly pleased, studied Stanbrook.

Vandenberg pushed aside the files, and pondered for a moment, finger-tips together. Then he turned to Huberman.

'I appreciate the point you made, Austin. If we withdrew the product completely, we should be up to our neck in trouble. Apart from the bad publicity, every woman who could get herself a shady lawyer would cook up some kind of claim—because you don't withdraw a product that sold over a million bottles in its first month unless there's something very drastically wrong with it. So we can't pull it completely. Yet we can't continue to market it as it is.'

'I won't take out STX-3,' put in Stanbrook quickly. 'All our claims are built around that one factor.'

'No. You won't take it out completely. But you'll cut it down to one-twentieth of its present strength.'

'One-twentieth. . . . Are you kidding? That won't do anything.'

'That's right. That's what I hope. No good, no harm. Now, listen to me. We've had a two months' run. We've built the following for Youth Elixir. Anything from now on is just consolidation. Well . . . The women who liked it in the first place will go back for more. And they'll be convinced that it's doing them the same amount of good, because when a woman looks into a mirror expecting to see something pleasant she *sees* something pleasant. The miracle happened before; she won't believe it isn't happening now; she couldn't bear to think that —maybe it was just her imagination, after all.

'And the rest—the women who didn't try Youth Elixir, in spite of the promotion . . . they'll come in, gradually. They are the younger women, the women who aren't reaching for every wonder cream the minute it hits the market. And they'll like the new formula. Youth Elixir is good, even without STX-3. Don't sell it short—it's a good cream.' He turned to Sarnoff. 'How does that sound to you, Harry.'

'It makes sense, boss.' Sarnoff nodded slowly. 'Sure, it makes sense.'

'Stanbrook?'

Stanbrook shrugged. 'If you've made up your mind. . . .'

'I think it's a good way out,' said Huberman. 'The only way out, possibly.'

'Okay. Then we're agreed. Now, as to details. Huberman, I want every available bottle pulled off the market, as discreetly

[118]

as possible. Say the perfume's wrong, or the consistency, or some damn thing. The new formula has to be ready for substitution immediately. You and Stanbrook get together on this and drop everything else. This has top priority. I want another meeting tomorrow, at . . . four-thirty'—checking his diary—'and at that time I want to hear your plans. They have to be precise and detailed.' He turned to Sarnoff. 'Now, Harry. Here's what I want you to do. See as many of these women'—waving a hand towards the files—'as possible. If they're amenable, get them into O'Malley's office. I want tests run. I don't care what it costs. I want to know exactly what is the mechanism of this business. Why STX-3 grows hair in some women and not in others. It may be that different types of skin need different concentrations of the extract. Maybe some people just shouldn't use it at all. But I want to *know*. I'm not giving up. STX-3 makes old skin young and we have to be able to use it. If we don't, someone else will.'

Harry nodded agreement. 'Okay, boss. I'll get after it. First priority.'

'One more thing. Tell O'Malley I want to know if STX-3 could be used to *make* hair grow—deliberately. On the scalp. If it could. . . .'

'We'd have it made.' Harry looked at him admiringly. Now, that was someone using his head. Why hadn't he thought of that?

Stanbrook was smiling unpleasantly. 'Maybe we should all get into white uniforms, and pretend we're in the pharmaceutical business. We used not to be so damned scientific, and look where we got.'

Vandenberg's voice was icy. 'Mr. Stanbrook. I wish you would remember something. You are not in a bath-tub operation any more. This is now a Vandenberg property.'

Stanbrook accepted the rebuke with his usual smile, but inside he was shaking. Bath-tub operation. All right, that's what it was. He wasn't ashamed of it. He'd mixed up the nail enamel in an old bath-tub in that office in the West Forties where the lift was always out of order and they even had to carry the goddamned stuff downstairs. They'd sweated blood to make this business, Louis and Harry and he. He'd made up the stuff and Louis had sold it, peddling it at first from door to door. And when a buyer was difficult, it was Louis who took him out to dinner and charmed him into a sale, and when that failed, Harry took the guy out—and not to dinner. Sure, they'd started the hard way. And now this damn, smug, fat-arsed moneybags sat there and sneered at him, Stanbrook, who made it all possible.

Sometimes he wondered why he stayed. He could get another job. Sure, any cosmetic company in the country would grab at the chance to have Marvin Stanbrook on their pay-roll.

But in his heart he knew why he stayed. There were new young men coming up. College degrees counted these days. Maybe if he went out to another company, after another job, they'd start checking into his record. Maybe they'd find that there never was a degree.

So what? Who needed to be a chemist to mix up a mess of make-up? Put coloured lard into a jar and you could sell it. It was only the package that counted. That and the perfume and the magic name—Vermeyers.

XIII

THE meeting broke up. As Sarnoff and the rest left, Vandenberg yawned. He was very tired.

There was a folder full of letters for signature upon his desk, and a tray full of incoming mail. He pulled the folder towards him, signed every letter and memorandum without reading one, and then took up the mail.

It was mostly routine. A letter from a woman who had a breathtakingly new idea for a compact. (It had been tried and discarded ten years ago.) The usual batch of invitations, including one from the wife of the Mayor of New York, and several from prominent society hostesses. He marked them all 'Decline'. The usual charity requests, reports from the heads of departments, and a bunch of inter-office memoranda. One of these caught his eye. It was a circular memo and it bore his own mimeographed, sprawling signature. It read briefly:

> The management regrets to notice that members of the female staff are wearing clothing unsuitable for office wear. It is requested that as of this date no girl shall wear sheer blouses, sunback dresses or any décolletage whatever during office hours.

And across the foot of the circular, written in red ink with an unmistakable flourish, were the words:

'Heil Hitler. May the men wear them?'

Even before he read the signature 'Sigrid Anderson' to the penned note he knew who had forwarded him the memo. A slow smile spread over his face. His hand went out deliberately to the intercom set.

'Get me the Personnel Director.'

When the telephone rang, he was still smiling. His voice was almost caressing.

'Mr. Pollovic. You send out memoranda over my name without my seeing them?'

There was a slight pause. Eugene Pollovic thought quickly what memoranda he had sent out recently.

'It's possible, sir. Company policy is always over your name.'

'But don't you think I should know and approve the policy before it is announced?'

'Why, certainly, sir. I can't remember any occasion when we have taken a new line without first securing your approval.'

'I have a memorandum before me now, Mr. Pollovic, of which I do not approve. I might say I consider it an exceedingly pompous and ridiculous document.'

Pollovic closed his eyes, waiting for the storm. He knew Vandenberg when he had that silky note in his voice. At the same time he was trying vainly to remember what could be the offending memorandum. Then a blast in his ear made him jump almost off his seat.

'Mr. Pollovic, this is a fashion house, not a girl's convent. I don't give a good goddamn what the girls wear, so long as they look attractive and clean. If there is any man in this office who can't keep his mind on his work when a girl wears a sheer blouse, get rid of him. Withdraw that memo!'

The receiver slammed down. Pollovic hung up gently, still trembling. He cursed softly and adequately. How had Vandenberg come to see that circular?

Vandenberg went through the rest of his mail, and rang for Miss Shaw. When she entered, he noticed for the first time what she was wearing. A pale blue sheer blouse. The slip beneath it was extremely decorative, and quite proper.

'That's a very attractive blouse, Miss Shaw.'

Her eyebrows went up in surprise. He never commented on her appearance.

'Why, thank you, Mr. Vandenberg.'

He handed her the circular. 'You can disregard that. It is being withdrawn.'

She met his eyes without even a twinkle. She was an extremely well trained secretary.

'Yes, sir.'

'Do I have any appointments for the next hour?'

'No—not until your dinner appointment.'

'Good. Will you please see that I am not disturbed. I should like to stretch out for a while.'

'Certainly, sir.'

She went over to the windows and drew the heavy curtains. She put out all the lights except the lamp on his desk. Then she left him.

At first he did not move, but sat looking at the darkened room. It seemed even larger in the shadows. A huge room for one man's office. And the desk too was enormous, a vast expanse of gleaming walnut. He felt insignificant and lonely.

Slowly his head turned, until he could see the empty space beyond the telephones where most executives would have had their photographs. He had never had a photograph upon his desk. No woman had ever lodged herself firmly enough in his life for him to want to have her likeness about him while he worked. And now, increasingly, he was aware of that lack. It was more than an empty space on his desk. It was an empty space within him.

He thought of Harry at the party. He liked Harry. He liked Harry more and more. That and nothing else had made him accept the invitation. He liked him because he was big. He was a self-made man, without any natural advantages, but he had the courage to stand up for himself, even with a man like Vandenberg. And he was loyal. Vandenberg knew that Vermeyers was more than a job to Harry; it was a second religion.

And Harry had a nice, unobtrusive wife and three attractive daughters. Sally wasn't the sort of wife he himself would have wanted, but she was a home-maker. There was an atmosphere of home all over the Sarnoff house, in spite of its lavish decorator-styled furnishings. He remembered the way young Sarah had automatically run to take his hat and offered to get him a drink. Perhaps daughters would have been better for him than a son. He overpowered a boy.

Well, he had no daughters, and no photograph upon his desk. Just four Japanese prints upon the wall. For a man with only a very little time left, it would have to be enough.

He drew himself up, took off his coat and trousers and, taking a robe from the closet where it was always kept, lay down on the couch.

[123]

He did not bother to lock the door. He knew the admirable, inconspicuous Miss Shaw would keep all callers at bay.

But the callers of the mind were beyond even her vigilance. He dreamt of his father, and Margot, his first wife, whom he had not thought of in years. And his father kept embracing Margot and the two of them laughed at him, tauntingly, and when he went to hit them they vanished, and there was only his own narrow bunk in the yacht, and he lay in it sleeplessly, alone, listening to the creaking of the vessel and the murmur of the water. Even in his dreams he was always alone, eventually.

XIV

SAM WOODSTOCK was happy. He had had a busy month, up to his neck in problems. He had hit upon a neat way to trap beauty salon distributors who bought merchandise only to bootleg it to unauthorized outlets; he had saved the company five thousand dollars a year in insurance premiums, by a simple rearrangement of their coverage; and now he was off with Sarnoff to the Retail Druggists' Cosmetic Convention.

This convention was the biggest of several that various members of the firm attended. It was held at Lake Champlain, and in mid-June the prospect was entrancing. They had a huge exhibit, with half a dozen girls to show off their products, and junketing would be the order of the day. The buyers from all the big independent stores would be there as well as the heads of the drugstore chains, seeking new ideas for their cosmetic departments. It was to be a big, five-day spree of goodwill and entertainment, and to Sam it was like Christmas to a child.

All was in readiness. The booth and display had gone on ahead, the reservations were made, they had their train tickets. In an hour they would be on their way. Only Sarnoff still wrestled with a problem. He was talking on the 'phone to Sally, his wife.

'Sally,' he said patiently, 'I know Ginny is playing at the concert. But she's only going to play for two minutes. Sarah can go in your place.... No, I don't think she *would* be that disappointed. I don't think so. No, I don't know it. All I know is that every time I want you with me for a convention you back out at the last minute!'

There was a pause while the unseen Sally argued. Sigrid Anderson, standing dutifully by, tried to keep the amusement out of her face. Every time ... Last December, for the medical convention, she got sick. A sudden attack of grippe. But this was midsummer. You couldn't have grippe in June. So Ginny, second youngest of Sarnoff's daughters, had a concert.

'Yes. . . . Yes. . . .' Sarnoff was casting his eyes up to the ceiling. He shrugged expressively, as though to say: What can you do? You can't fight City Hall. 'Sally. Listen to me. You gotta remember something. This kid ain't no genius. She's just a nice, nine-year-old kid. She doesn't play too well. Money we'll never make with this kid. A Padaroosky she'll never be. Maybe she's tone-deaf. . . . No, I don't want her marked for life. I don't want her to feel she's rejected. Oh. . . . That so? Well, if a psychiatrist says so, of course it's so. We mustn't mark her. Okay, Sally. Okay, okay. You go to the concert. I'll go to the Convention. Good-bye.'

He put down the receiver, firmly and emphatically. To the instrument, he muttered: 'So now it's a psychiatrist. Do I want my child marked for life? Am I an unnatural father? Does Veremyers mean more to me than my own flesh and blood? Jesus Christ, Ziggie, who does she think pays for her mink coat and her Cadillac and the kids' schooling? Wives . . . Christ Almighty!"

'You shouldn't try to force her,' Ziggie said smoothly. Ziggie was always on the side of the boss's wife. He knew it, and enjoyed it, because he knew Sally liked it. 'She just doesn't like that gin-swilling crowd, and I don't blame her.'

'You'd like to go.'

'Sure. But that's because I know I can't. I'm human, too.'

He chuckled richly. 'You'd like it, even if you could go. I could do with you, too. I need someone along like you. Entertaining without a woman ain't easy.'

'But it wouldn't be good if your secretary were the woman.'

'Sure. It's a good rule, I know it. I ain't kicking. But I sure as hell wish Sally would get her fanny out there with me for just one of these damn Conventions.'

Sam Woodstock put his head around the door.

'All ready? We should be leaving.'

'Sure, I'm ready. Okay, dollface, take care of the office for us.'

He gave her a rough hug, and Sam deposited a light kiss on the side of her cheek. She patted them both on the back.

'Have a good trip. Enjoy yourselves. And think of me— once.'

[126]

'Sure. We'll send you some water from the lake!'

And Sarnoff went out, roaring with laughter at his own joke.

The office seemed very quiet when they had gone. Ziggie sighed, then laughed. Actually she had no desire to accompany Sarnoff on any of his trips. But she was careful not to let him know this. If he had suspected it, he would have moved heaven and earth to alter the company rule that forbade executives taking their secretaries on trips with them. And when Sarnoff moved, events had a curious way of falling into the pattern of his desires.

It was three weeks since the conference on Youth Elixir. The big switch was taking place, smoothly and imperceptibly. Still the cases came in; seventy-four this week. It was a measure of Sarnoff's confidence in her that he left her alone in the office at such a time. She would be busy. Every letter had to be answered, every woman who could be brought into the office interviewed. Sarnoff had told her: 'If you have any problems, go straight to the boss. He knows you're taking care of things.'

She was exhausted. It had been a busy week. Preparations for the Convention were always strenuous, and this business of Youth Elixir on top of them had meant overtime every night for a week. She glanced at her watch. Five-forty-five. She wouldn't work tonight. There was always Monday.

She was putting away the trays of work, when Paul Vandenberg entered.

'Good evening. Mr. Sarnoff gone already?'

'Yes, sir. He left for the Convention. They'll be setting up the booths over the weekend.'

'Oh, of course. I had forgotten.'

He did not go, as she expected, but instead leaned against a table, looking around the room, his arms folded across his chest.

'Is there . . . anything I can do, sir?'

At first, he did not answer. He seemed preoccupied. Then he stared at her in an odd, unsmiling fashion.

'I don't know,' he said. Then, almost unwillingly: 'Do you have an engagement tonight?'

'No,' she answered unthinkingly, expecting him to ask her to undertake some task.

[127]

'Then you can do something for me. I was looking for a companion for dinner.'

Until he said it he was not himself aware of what he was going to say. Immediately the words were out, he asked himself: Now why did I say that? I don't even know this girl.

He had noticed lately an increasing tendency in himself to act on whim. It bothered him. He had always been a man of deliberate, planned actions. But with a mental shrug, he answered his unspoken question: Why not? It may not be wise. But what difference does it make?

He hated dining alone. Tonight a last-minute change of plans had left him with an empty evening. He remembered, looking at Sigrid Anderson, the night he had the heart attack. She was kind—very kind.

The ingenuousness of his reply had taken her off guard. Excitement sparkled in her eyes and confusion brought the swift colour to her cheeks. He noticed both.

'Thank you,' she said breathlessly. It seemed the wrong way to accept an invitation, but the invitation itself was scarcely formal.

'Are you finished here?'

'Yes. I was just going to lock up.'

'Then how about meeting me downstairs in half an hour. Or better—in the Plaza lounge. My car is parked there.'

'All right.'

Again she knew it was not the right thing to say. He would think her an idiot. But her heart was pounding. She was glad he gave her time to wash. Her face was hot and shining from a hard afternoon's work, and she wished she were wearing something more festive than a simple black cotton dress.

She was too astonished to ask herself if dining with Vandenberg were wise. She was like a sleep-walker. The impossible had happened.

He was already waiting for her when she arrived. She saw him before he saw her. (She noticed that he was not watching the door. He appeared quite lost in thought.) She had a vivid, visual impression of him that stayed with her for a long while afterwards, of a distinguished and remote man in a conservative, pale grey suit. He might have been a diplomat.

[128]

She approached him, smiling, apparently at her ease.

'Did I keep you waiting?'

'The result was worth it,' he replied gravely. 'What will you have?'

'Scotch, please. On the rocks.'

He ordered the same. Over the drinks she observed him shyly, then looked away again. He seemed to have shaken off his preoccupation, and there was mockery in his eyes. She did not know whether it was for her or for himself.

'You are quite impulsive, aren't you?' she asked him unexpectedly.

'Not always.' He smiled. 'But as I grow older—there seems less and less point in weighing what I do.'

'If we are seen we shall be talked about.'

'Does it bother you?'

'No.'

'Good. Then we shall forget the possibility.'

In spite of the trembling of her hands, she found it astonishingly easy to talk to him. She kept reminding herself, This is I, Sigrid Anderson, having cocktails with Paul Vandenberg.

'You must be very lonely,' she said bluntly.

'I am sure it is not only lonely men who invite you out to dinner.'

'No. But they're not men like you.'

'You are still befuddled by the sixty million,' he retorted cuttingly.

'It's not only that. It's everything about you. You are . . . different.'

After her second drink (he simply toyed with his), he asked her if she drove. When, surprised, she answered 'yes', he said briskly:

'Good. Then we'll take my car and you can be my chauffeur. I let Jim go.'

Jim Mahoney was Vandenberg's chauffeur; he seldom drove himself, no doubt because of his heart condition. She felt terrified at the thought of driving his big Cadillac. However, she would have died rather than confess it.

'Do you know the Island?' he asked.

'Fairly well.'

'Well enough to follow my instructions? There's a place I like near Cold Spring Harbour.'

'Oh, yes, I know that route well. In the summer we often hire a car for the weekend and we usually go to the North Shore beaches.'

' "We"?'

'My room-mate and I.' It amused her that he caught at that 'we'.

'I see. Well, let's go. I don't like hotel lounges.'

Outside, a doorman obsequiously ran off to fetch his car. They did not speak. As she settled herself at the wheel, he laughed softly.

'It's insured, you know. And my life isn't worth much. So that leaves only yourself you have to worry about.'

She bit her lip. She had not realized her nervousness was so apparent.

'I'll try to take good care of myself,' she said lightly.

Once they were moving, however, she forgot the strangeness of his car. She loved to drive and the power of this sleek monster captivated her. This—this was the sheer, ultimate joy of motion. She was even unaware, for a while, of the man beside her.

They drove without speaking. He was completely relaxed, sitting low in the seat, his head resting on the back. When she thought of him again, she wondered if he were sleeping. An unexpected tenderness welled up in her. She felt as she had before, when she put him to bed. There was something vulnerable and helpless about him, in spite of his power. Pride that she could help him vied with wistfulness at the thought of the little she could do; there was an ache inside her. The thought sprang into her mind: I'd like to drive this beautiful car miles and miles and miles, and take him away from the business and the problems and all the things that are tormenting him.

Yes, but you couldn't give him health, something reminded her.

So she put these thoughts away. There was just this car, which was becoming a part of her with every mile they covered, and the other cars on the road, and lights, and the unfolding ribbon of road leading them away from Fifth Avenue and The House of Vermeyer, into the green stillness of Long Island.

The place that he knew was a small hotel beyond Cold Spring Harbour. It was an old Colonial building, well off the main route and hidden by a grove of tall pines. Unless one were directed to it, it would be impossible to find. The restaurant was both excellent and expensive.

Vandenberg seemed to be well known there, and as they followed the head waiter to a table a small cloud descended upon the evening. It must have shown in her face, for over another cocktail he suddenly looked at her with his direct, all-seeing glance, then smiled.

'Yes, I do come here often. Usually for a weekend. Alone.'

She blushed. 'I don't know what to say to that.'

'So say nothing.'

'You must think me a fool.'

'No. I think you're very charming. And delightfully young.'

'I wish I were not so young.'

'Why wish away your most precious possession? Youth goes so quickly, anyway.'

She looked about her. 'It's wonderfully quiet here. Is that why you stay?'

'Yes. In Fairfield I can never get away from Vermeyers, thanks to the telephone. Not even Sarnoff knows about this place. When things get too much, I come out here, and lie in bed and listen to the pines. Have you ever heard pines outside your window at night?'

She shook her head.

'They creak in the wind. It's the oddest sound. And above it is a high, singing whisper. It's one of the loneliest sounds in the world, and yet I like it.'

She wished she could hear the pines, with him. And then she hastily busied herself with her drink, in case that thought too should show on her tell-tale face.

'Ziggie,' he said.

'Yes?'

'I didn't authorize that memo.'

[131]

For a moment she stared at him, then laughter burst in her eyes. 'About the blouses?'

'Yes. About the blouses. I killed it.'

She laughed helplessly. It was a relief to give way to even this show of feeling. She was tense.

He proved to be a charming dinner companion. She had expected him to be morose or absorbed. Instead he talked lightly on a dozen different subjects, until she was completely at her ease.

At one point, when she was addressing him, she started to say: 'Mr. Vandenberg. . . .'

He interrupted her. 'Don't you think that's a little formal for this setting?'

'Very formal.'

'Well then, try Paul, so long as we're not in the office.'

'Paul. . . .' It sounded so strange that she was immediately shy again, and she hesitated, then went on, not looking at him: 'Why did you ask me to come out with you tonight?'

He considered for a moment, staring at her averted face. Quite beautiful, he was thinking. Why hadn't I noticed before?

'I suppose—because you're a human being, with a mind of your own. You're a beautiful woman, and I like that. But you're also a person. Very few women are.'

'You *were* lonely.'

'Oh yes. That's a more or less constant condition. And I suppose you've heard tales of the way I meet it.'

'There is—talk.'

'My asking you to keep me company tonight—wasn't in line with the talk.'

Coming from another man, the words might have been meaningless. But instinctively she knew that this man could not be bothered to dissemble.

They walked in the garden after dinner, a place intoxicatingly sweet with the perfume of honeysuckle and June roses. They were very quiet. Neither felt the need for speech. This silent communion was oddly satisfying to him. Too many women would have felt they had to talk.

On the long drive back, they were still silent. He noticed how well she drove, and that too was pleasing.

'Ziggie. I owe you an apology. I was quite insulting when I was drunk.'

'No. Just drunk.'

'You couldn't be Sarnoff's mistress.'

She smiled enigmatically at the unwinding road. 'No. I couldn't be.'

He put his head back again and closed his eyes. The wind beat against the car, and the high hedges and tall trees flashed past them as the speedometer needle crept up to sixty. And all the way the sweetness of honeysuckle was in their nostrils.

Too soon they were engulfed by the traffic of Queens, and the magic of the June night dissolved in honking cars, neon lights, and the odours of the city. They partly recaptured the spell on Grand Central Parkway, but it was a different spell. It was the restless surge of movement, speeding cars, the encroaching life of the great city. They found themselves talking again.

At his apartment she insisted on leaving the car and taking a cab home. There was a complete lack of feminine caprice about her that delighted him. And when he finally had said good-bye to her and gone up to his empty rooms, he found himself remembering a dozen small gestures and mannerisms that at the time he scarcely had noticed.

He also found himself speculating on the young men she would undoubtedly know, and was surprised to find his speculations quite distasteful.

XV

FRANCESCA ALBERTSON (she had been born plain Frances Jones) was in her element. Girls were parading before her, hands held rigidly in front of them, dutifully following her instructions. This was a special test. On one hand a new protective cream was being placed, and then each hand was striped with various staining materials—ink, paint, carbon, lipstick. The white, well-manicured hands took on a barbaric quality. Like the war-paint of savages, the streaks of colour seemed to lend an alien, fantastic beauty to the pale skin they adorned.

Once the hands were duly striped, each would be washed separately, dried, washed again—the solemn ritual being repeated a dozen times. At the end of the test, the victims' hands would no longer be white, but valuable data would be accumulated for the research files of the laboratory.

Francesca Albertson was in charge of consumer research. It was her job to investigate what the public wanted and whether what it wanted was good for it. Newcomers to The House of Vermeyer still looked upon her with awe, as a symbol of the heights to which a girl could rise in this business. Starting some eighteen years before as secretary to Louis Vermeyer, she was now one of the top executives. But to Sigrid Anderson she was a symbol of something else. She smiled too readily and too viciously; she was too quick to defend the prerogatives of her position; she was too jealous of younger, newer women. Insecurity had etched fine, bitter lines at the corners of her mouth, prompted the nervous flutterings of her ageing hands, sharpened the edge in her voice. That's a career woman, Ziggie reminded herself.

Ziggie was watching her now, as her own hands were painted. The sparse hair, dragged back into a false chignon, would have been grey but for the too pretty honey-coloured tint she used. The dry skin was papery and lined and her cosmetics too heavily applied. Although probably forty-five, she looked much older. Not for the first time, Ziggie wondered: How does she hang on to her position? She can't even apply her own make-up.

Ziggie had neither seen Vandenberg nor spoken to him since their dinner together, almost a week ago. Each day she had expected him to call her, and when the inter-office phone rang she leapt to it, trembling. But it had not once been Vandenberg.

She was sleeping badly. The days went by slowly and the evenings seemed empty. When she awoke in the morning, Paul (as she now called him in her thoughts) was the first person in her mind. Wonderingly, she began to ask herself: Is this—love? This glow and excitement—this sick emptiness. . . . Are they both part of the business one calls being in love?

The door behind her opened, recalling her from her reverie, and then she was trembling violently. She knew, even before he spoke, that Paul had entered. It was reflected in the sudden change that came over Albertson.

'How's it going?'

Francesca smiled effusively. The mouth turned upwards, the lines about it deepening, but there was no warmth in the eyes. They remained cold, malicious, watchful.

'Wonderful, Mr. Vandenberg. Simply wonderful. It's a terrific product.'

He came over, taking Ziggie's hands in his, and at the same time smiled at her.

'Hello, Miss Anderson.'

'Good afternoon, sir.'

She felt radiant, glowing from top to toe. The firmness of his fingers holding hers seemed to communicate a secret message to her body.

'They seem sore.'

'They've had six washings. At the end of twelve, I'll have no hands!'

She spoke cheerfully, but Francesca's smile became fixed and venomous.

'But you see how faint the discolorations are on the right hand, Mr. Vandenberg. The cream does a terrific job—makes the stains float right off!'

[135]

'It's not good enough, Miss Albertson. The difference isn't marked enough. I saw Miss Shaw's hands, too—same thing, chapped. Both of them. Let me see your tables.'

He ran down the charts she handed him, ticking off the names of several girls.

'I want to see these girls—have them come into my office right away. And send all the reports in to me just as soon as you have them ready.'

'Certainly, sir.'

Why does she try to fool him, Ziggie wondered? You can't fool Vandenberg with an inferior product. He's too jealous of his name.

At the door he turned to her.

'When does Mr. Sarnoff get back?'

'He'll be back in town tomorrow. In the office Monday.'

'Everything been okay?'

'Perfectly. Very quiet. Not too many cases.'

'Good. I'd like to see what you have. Come into my office at five-fifteen with anything that has come in since he left.'

'Yes, sir.'

At five-fifteen he was not ready. Miss Shaw informed her that he was tied up, but had left word that she was to wait for him.

She waited. At six-thirty he was finally free. Miss Shaw had gone, and he himself telephoned for her to come in. She gathered up her papers and walked through the now empty offices.

He had taken off his shoes, and had a glass of whisky in his hand when she entered. He was busy pouring a second glass from a decanter that he had taken from a closet. He smiled disarmingly.

'Come in and sit down. Oh, put the papers over there. We won't need them.'

She was disconcerted, as much by his stockinged feet as by his words.

'I thought—you wanted to go over them. . . .'

He smiled again. 'I'll take your word for it that things are okay.' He indicated the couch and handed her a glass. 'To your very good health.'

'To yours,' she responded automatically, and then could have bitten her tongue out.

'Mine isn't worth drinking to,' he said lightly.

She sat down, rather self-consciously, and he took his place beside her. He downed his drink quickly and shook himself.

'Brrrr. That feels better. You're not drinking.'

'I can't take it that fast. But it's good.'

He was watching her and she wished he wouldn't.

'Do you have any plans for the evening?'

'No.'

'Do you think you might like to have dinner with me again?'

Her heart was pounding. Almost inaudibly, she answered:

'Yes—I think I might.'

She knew she shouldn't say yes. She should say no, and get out of there as quickly as possible. He was different tonight. The almost bored air had gone. He was keenly alert, unmistakably amused at something—perhaps at her. In a rush, the stories that were told about him came back to her. He was a philanderer. Did he think she was another Gloria Vernon? And at the same time she thought (ridiculously) of her mother and father. What would they say if they knew their daughter was embarking on an affair with a middle-aged man who regarded an amour as a mere after-dinner entertainment?

But she did not retract. Instead, she sat sipping her straight whisky and trying to act as though she liked it. And defiantly she told her inward critic: You're taking a heck of a lot for granted. He has only asked me to have dinner with him. And who says I'm starting an affair with him? He knows I'm not that sort of a girl.

They had dinner in town. This time they took a cab and she was glad, because he had poured her a stiff drink and she felt light-headed. They went to a small but very elegant French place, and Ziggie again wished she were wearing something chic. It was exasperating not to be able to make herself pretty for him.

But as though he read her thoughts he said quietly:

'You look so lovely. You make all these others look—overblown.'

He bought her a spray of gardenias, and the heady perfume

entranced her. Never afterwards would she be able to smell gardenias without thinking of Paul Vandenberg.

Time sped on, too fast. She wanted to stop it. It was like the bubbles in the champagne she was drinking. Every bubble was a minute, rising, bursting, vanishing. And when the last glass was empty, the evening would be over.

But it was not over. He asked her:

'Would you like a drive?'

'Yes, please. By the river.'

'You like the river at night, too?'

'Yes, that's when I love New York. When all the lights are sparkling and the offices are dark.'

On a sudden impulse, he told the taxi-driver to drive down-town. The wind off the water was cool, and boat sirens wailed to them with a melancholy insistence. The air was full of night noises. At South Ferry he paid off the cab, and said simply:

'Let's go over to Staten Island. I haven't done this for years.'

They held hands as they went through the turnstile, and he was no longer remote. He watched the people around them, and appeared like a man to whom everything was new. As they made their way forward, he said suddenly:

'I wish there were someone here selling roast chestnuts.'

'Why roast chestnuts?'

'When I was a boy my father used to bring me into New York, and then forget me. I always slipped away and took the ferry-boat. There was usually a hurdy-gurdy man and a chest-nut vendor on board. The music of the hurdy-gurdy and the smell of the chestnuts. . . .' He broke off, and laughed. 'Silly, isn't it?'

'I always wanted to come to New York when I was a child. I read all I could about it. I used to dream of the wonderful things I'd do here, when I finally escaped from St. Paul.'

'And now you find you've fled one prison for another.'

'No.' She looked at him in surprise. 'Why do you think of it as a prison?'

He shrugged. 'All places are prisons. We establish our own routines, we appoint our own guards. Perhaps—perhaps only children are free.'

'But I feel I'm free.'

[138]

He smiled at her, quizzically. 'Yes, you are still a child. That is your greatest charm.'

She was not sure she was pleased with that. She thought of herself as a worldling. After all, had she not become a cosmopolitan, a member of the exotic, fast, sophisticated world that was called New York?

They were cutting through the water now, the ferry lifting slightly with the river swell. She leaned her elbows on the rail, staring at the rippling water glittering in the moonlight. The Statue of Liberty rose before them, powerful arm upraised, and then slid away into the shadows. It was wonderfully cool on the water, and she closed her eyes, content with the motion of the boat, the breeze, the murmuring of the water and the physical nearness of the man standing beside her.

'What do we do when we get there?' she asked, after a while.

'Come back. It's only the ride which is magic.'

'Yes. It *is* magic. Paul . . . I don't know you at all, do I?'

'Do you want to?'

His eyes were staring into hers, sombre now. Aware of a heavier beating in her breast, she whispered:

'Yes.'

She knew that she committed herself in that moment. And still her mind insisted: Yes, yes. She could not turn back now.

He put his arms around her, one hand pressing her against him so that she trembled violently at the contact with his body. He did not kiss her at once, but still looked into her face.

'You're sure it's yes?' he asked quietly.

She nodded. She could not speak.

She closed her eyes as he kissed her. Her fingers dug into his back, and her mouth opened. His kiss hurt her, and she enjoyed the hurt of it.

Afterwards, he still held her closely against him, one hand playing with her breasts. There was no one near them and they might have been alone in the shadows. She felt shaken and weak with excitement.

They rode back silently, and a sense of unreality possessed her as she followed him through the turnstile for the second time. The clicking of the dime in the coin box, the noise of

[139]

cars going aboard, the scampering of children on the wooden deck—all formed a pattern of unreality.

On the long cab ride uptown fear and desire warred within her. I have to, I have to, she told herself. If I turn back now, I'm a coward. I love him. I love him so much it has to be right. This is the thing we all wait for.

And yet there were the other thoughts that fought with her love. She remembered her parents. She remembered her own cool creed, the unshakeable belief upon which her anticipations of the future were built: Marriage, then love. Oh, God, she thought, there should be a wedding. White satin and flowers, and music, and Mother being so happy. . . .

But this man is different. And I love him. Right or wrong, I love him.

He pulled her to him and kissed her again, and in the darkness of the cab they were free as they had not been on the ferry. He laughed softly at her responsiveness.

'I was wrong. You're not a child.'

'Paul. I love you.'

She whispered it desperately. She felt lonely in her love for him. He didn't understand. This was nothing to him. Oh Paul, Paul, this is different. . . . You have to see, it's different.

When they were in his apartment, vast, luxurious and discreetly lit, shyness returned to her. She stared at him with wide eyes and a tragic mouth. He was urbane, matter-of-fact.

'Here'—reaching into his closet—'one of my robes might be useful. A little large, perhaps.'

He smiled at her, gently, understandingly—oh, how understandingly. He touched her cheek with a forefinger.

'How about a drink?'

She clutched at that, pathetically. 'Oh yes, please. I'd love one.'

He poured two, and she gulped hers down before she noticed that he had scarcely sipped his but put it aside. Idiotically, she thought: I wish I weren't still a virgin. He'll probably be disappointed. It suddenly seemed very ridiculous that she had thought such a matter important, and clung so insistently hitherto to her inviolability.

She perched on the arm of a chair. She noticed it was sherry he had poured for her.

'Sherry by Candlelight,' she said involuntarily.

He laughed. 'Yes. Sorry about the candles. I don't think I could rustle any up at such short notice. Funny. We use them as symbols all the time and I don't think I've seen any in years outside of restaurants.'

'I use them always—when I have company for dinner.'

'They *are* charming. Will you invite me for dinner some evening?'

She knew he was talking to give her time. She was grateful for his poise. It would be intolerably awkward with a younger man. She remembered the long succession of dreary young men she had dated, and reflected: If it were one of them, we'd both be embarrassed.

She wondered: How do we get to the point? In books it always seemed so easy. At one moment hero and heroine were drinking, whispering in each other's ear; and then, suddenly, there were no clothes. She wished they could skip like that. She had never undressed before a man.

He opened what appeared to be a bar set in the wall, and revealed a gramophone. He selected an album, with obvious care, and placed the record on the spindle.

It was a Bach concerto. For a moment he stood near the instrument, staring ahead of him. She wondered if he had forgotten her. Then he came over, tilted her face upwards, and kissed her very lightly on the forehead.

'I'll smoke a cigar while I wait,' he said softly. 'Don't be long.'

And it was as easy as that. She picked up the robe and went through to the bathroom. The music had an oddly calming effect upon her, and she left the door open so that she might hear it. So we both like Bach, she thought.

When she emerged from the bathroom he was in bed. He had piled the pillows high behind him, and he smiled and held out a hand to her.

'Come here.'

She advanced slowly, holding his robe about her. Just out of reach of his hand, she stood still, very erect.

'Paul—I'm sorry. I know men don't like virgins. I am one.'

For a moment he stared up at her, surprised. She thought

he looked angry. Then the hard, bright look faded and his expression became one of mingled sorrow and suffering, bitterness and a tenderness that she could not fathom. He reached up, caught her and drew her down against him. He nuzzled the top of her head with his cheek, caressing her body very gently with his hand. He whispered:

'Don't be afraid, Sigrid. There's only a little pain.'

'I'm not afraid—with you. But. . . . Do you mind?'

He smiled above her head, crookedly.

'No. I don't mind.'

Dear God, he thought, what am I getting into now?

XVI

HARRY SARNOFF was not dissatisfied with his lot. He had come far. From a five-year-old immigrant boy to a fifty-thousand-a-year executive—it wasn't bad for his forty-seven years in the States. Not that he thought much about that immigrant boy. Since the cold war he preferred to forget his Russian origins and refer to himself as an American born. Sarnoff was a sufficiently ambiguous name in a country of ambiguous names.

There were times, however, when his satisfaction was not complete. He was Vice-President of an immensely successful company, but he had no stock-holding. Louis had always played it close. He had treated Harry as though he were on the same footing as Stanbrook, for example. Stanbrook, of course, felt that he had played a decisive part in the building of Vermeyers, but Sarnoff knew better. To be a cosmetic chemist —that was easy. Like falling off a log. Any chemicker could have played Stanbrook's part. And what had he ever done but get them into trouble? And when he got them into trouble, who got them out? Sarnoff. Sarnoff the fixer.

Sarnoff had never gotten around to an education. There had not been time. Even when he was a boy, there was always the newspaper round, the crap games where he usually managed to pick up enough nickels and dimes to buy the Sunday dinner, the delivery service rounds for the local stores. There was always the family to provide for, and Harry had seemed to be a natural provider. When his Pa died, it had been Harry who took over, child though he was, and as he grew into precocious young manhood it was to Harry that his sister Becky turned, and his cousins, and even his dead father's brothers and sisters. Because Harry had the golden touch, Harry was lucky.

But he knew luck wasn't all. He had something which he himself could not have defined, something that took the place of a formal education and put him way up above the other guys. It was an innate shrewdness. It was knowing the other fellow's weakness, knowing when to get out of a poker game, knowing the right moment to stake the pile. Call it flair, call it insight. It paid off.

For Vermeyer it had paid off richly. Looking back, it seemed to Sarnoff that their joint careers had been a long succession of crises and triumphs—triumphs engineered by Sarnoff. But their relationship had changed, subtly. At first, Sarnoff had been the lucky guy, the fellow with the cash, the one to finance the dream; then gradually Vermeyer had drawn even, had grown from a shabby, half-starved boy into a successful business man. And as he grew, even though it had been Sarnoff who made it all possible, he grew away from his friend. There was a widening gulf between them. Their minds did not move in the same way, did not hold the same dreams. Sarnoff, aware of his limitations, didn't resent it. Sure, that was Vermeyer. That was the big streak that he himself had been smart enough to see and stake. Okay, he was the boss.

But maybe the boss had forgotten, now and then, how much he owed to his Vice-President. It wasn't only the money that started the company. There was that time, back in the early days, when they got in trouble with the Police Department because of that lousy room they first used as a factory. Fire-trap the police called it, and fire-trap it was. But it tided them over, when the dough wasn't so easy. And thanks to Sarnoff's little deal with the inspectors they were allowed to use it.

And then there were the labour disputes. No one could handle the men the way Sarnoff handled them. He had a gift for it. They loved him. Even now, there wasn't one of the old gang who didn't speak of him with respect and affection. Harry had the human touch which Vermeyer had lacked. He could swear at you and browbeat you and even cheat you—and yet you loved him, because he took an interest in your family and your problems, he was ready with a fast loan if you were in a jam, he could shut an eye if you needed some time off for an emergency. Yes, it had been Harry who had kept the staff together when they were all overworked and underpaid.

And the doctors. . . . Where would The House of Vermeyer be today if it hadn't been for the doctors? And who had been

[144]

smart enough to see, even eighteen years ago, that cosmetics had to have the blessing of the medical profession?

Sarnoff knew how to influence people and win friends. He never had to read the book, he even could have taught the writers a thing or two. You wanted theatre tickets for a top show? He could get them. You wanted a hotel room when the city was convention-full? He could arrange it. You just wanted a good evening, with a steak dinner and plenty of liquor and a companion at gin rummy who didn't mind losing? Sure, he could give you that too. He could even find a girl for you, when that was the requirement.

Sarnoff had become a power. Big men were his intimates, not only in business but in the fields of medicine and politics. A helpful word from him, and the way became smooth; oppose him, and he could break you. Very few people opposed him, and certainly none of the young doctors with a career to make in dermatology.

But that was water over the dam now. He was like a cobbler who had done his work too well, and starved for lack of shoes to mend. Vermeyers didn't really need him any more; their procedures were checked and counter-checked and even if a mistake were made occasionally the remedy was ready to hand. They were too big now. Nobody could touch them.

And Vandenberg didn't know the half of what Sarnoff had done. He just couldn't know what Louis had owed to him. It was an unfair world.

Harry sat in his office late one evening, pondering the unfairness of it. Ziggie and Sam had gone—he had sent them home. It was one of those days when he felt, as he would have put it, low. Not for any particular reason. It just seemed to him that he hadn't got out of life what he ought to have done. And he wanted someone to be around to share in his gloom.

If Ziggie had been sincere, now, he would have taken her out to dinner. That would have been nice. She was a smart kid, and a looker. But she wasn't sincere. She always pretended to feel sorry for him when he was low, and thought he didn't see that it was only pretence. Same as she always asked after his health if she thought he was feeling sick, all tenderness. And always it would end up the same way: she'd suggest he should take a trip to Florida. Sure, she got rid of him that way. He knew it. He was a sucker for sympathy. Someone only had to start commiserating with him and telling him he looked sick, and he *felt* sick. He'd remember how hard he worked, how hard he played, he'd remember the people he had known who had just dropped dead at their desk or over a game of golf or in bed. Sure, he was sick. He was tired. And it only needed someone to remind him of it and he couldn't hold on any longer.

Only Ziggie shouldn't oughta laugh about it with Sam. He knew she did. She just wasn't sincere.

At that moment there was a step in the outer office. He looked up, and Gloria Vernon was peering round the door.

Instantly he was all smiles.

'Hiya, honey. Come on in. Where you been hiding?'

'Hi, Harry.' She looked jaded, and she came in slowly and slid into a seat. 'Oh, I've been around.'

'You don't come in and see me any more.'

'I've been busy. Trying to get my classes in shape.'

He saw the circles under her eyes, the tired droop of her back. Poor kid. She was trying. She sure was trying.

'The boss is pleased with you, Gloria. He told me.'

It was a lie, but he thought she needed some encouragement. Her response was a cynical shrug.

'Am I supposed to turn handsprings?'

'Now, Gloria, don't be like that. That ain't nice.'

'Oh, no, I know. I'm not nice. The big boss has been very good to me, and I should go around saying "Thank you, Mr. Vandenberg. Thank you very much, Mr. Vandenberg".'

He watched her shrewdly.

'Gloria, honey, it don't pay for people like you and me to hate our bread and butter.'

'I don't care.' Her tone was completely lethargic. 'Maybe for you it's different. But I—I just don't care any more.'

'That ain't smart, Gloria. And if it's because of Louis, he wasn't worth it. No man is.'

She drew in her breath sharply. 'You shouldn't say that. You *knew* him.'

'Sure. We both knew him. And he wouldn't marry you, would he? So why go around messing up your life for someone that wouldn't marry you? Louis was a bum, that way. No good shutting your eyes to it. He was just a bum.'

He meant to hurt her. He knew it would be good for her. Sometimes you just had to hurt people to get the pressure broken down. Harry didn't know how he knew these things, but he did.

Gloria put her hands over her face, and sobbed once. He sat and watched her, watched her shoulders heaving. Then she straightened up.

'No. I won't cry. I've cried so much. And it makes me look awful.'

'You ain't crying for Louis, kid.'

'What am I crying for, Harry?'

Somehow she never minded when Harry spoke to her like this. Harry had always been her friend. When she was just a raw kid, always she had turned to Harry when she needed help, and Harry had helped. He was rough but he was kind.

'You're crying because you've toppled, kid. This world was a big bright shiny ball and you on top of it, and now you've toppled. And you ain't doing nothing about it. Just crying.'

'You don't understand, Harry. I loved Louis.'

'Horseshit.' If there had been a spittoon, Harry would have spat.

Her eyes were misty and her voice low.

'You never knew him the way I knew him, Harry. He wasn't hard with me. He was wonderfully tender and gentle. He was sensitive. I understood him. Sadie never understood him. He turned to me because he had to. There was nothing in his life.'

She doesn't believe it, he thought. She knows Louis was always horsing it up with a dozen women. She was just top girl, that's all. That's why they fought. She wanted it to be the way she thinks it was. She wanted him to love her. That's why she wanted him to divorce Sadie and marry her. To show the rest of us she was more than top girl.

'Come along, honey,' he said abruptly. 'I'll buy you dinner. Where would you like to eat?'

'Oh—anywhere.' She looked up at him as he came and stood in front of her. 'Harry, you're a sweet guy.'

'I'm a bum,' he said. He let out a throaty chuckle, pulled her to her feet and held her to him. 'Just a bum. Only reason I don't make a pass at you is you're too damn tall. I forgot my Adlers!' And he let out his familiar guffaw and slapped her on the behind.

They ate at 'La Fourchette'. They had often eaten there before. When they had been working late with Louis on new promotions and Louis had had other people in town, Harry had often taken her there. It was a place they both liked and felt at home in.

They didn't take a cab to the restaurant. Harry felt it would be good to walk. He had an intuitive knowledge of what people needed, and he knew that what Gloria needed just now was silence and companionship. Harry couldn't be subtle. He couldn't change his conversation to what a girl like Gloria wanted to hear, but he knew when to keep his mouth shut. So they walked, quietly.

It was hot in the city streets. People moved slowly, listlessly. The girls were wearing low-cut summer cottons that almost showed their nipples. Sarnoff watched them unthinkingly as they sauntered crosstown. Some dolls. Part of the city. Nowhere but in New York would you see kids dress like that, even for work. Well, it was okay. It was part of the stamp of the fabulous city. He loved it. He loved every stone, every smell, every sound, everything that was New York. This was the city that had made him a fifty-thousand-a-year man. This was the promised land.

The restaurant was crowded, but he was known there, and they were at once shown to a good table. His spirits were rising with each moment. Sure, life wasn't so bad. Some people appreciated him. Gloria, for instance. And Gloria was a gorgeous doll. Men still turned to look at her. Now, under the lights, you didn't even see the shadows under her eyes. She was feeling better already.

Gloria had snails, and felt much better. And Harry broke up the crisp French bread and mopped up the butter and garlic sauce from her snails and ate it slobberingly, ordering more for her.

'Why don't you have snails, Harry?'

[148]

'Don't like 'em,' he muttered from a mouth stuffed with bread.

She smiled at him, an April smile that made her deep blue eyes incredibly beautiful. Same old Harry. Always stealing the things off her plate because he didn't like them enough to order them for himself.

'This is like old times, isn't it, Harry?'

'Yeah. But it don't do no good to think about old times, kid.'

'How do you stop?'

'Vandenberg's a good guy. You could do a job for him.'

'He doesn't trust me.'

'You ain't given him no cause to. That was a pretty stupid thing to do—getting plastered at my party.'

'I didn't mean to, Harry. It just happened.'

'Sure. It always does. That's why he won't trust you.'

She sat staring tensely over his head for a moment. He knew she had something on her mind. Finally it came out.

'Harry.'

'Yeah?'

'You know about the T.V. programme.'

At first he did not answer. This was one he hadn't expected. Sure, he knew about the T.V. programme. But he hadn't thought she did.

'What about it, kid?' His tone was innocence itself.

'P. V. has got it all set up. Without even letting me know. Not only am I not to be a part of it, but he doesn't even tell me.'

'Who told you about it?'

'What does it matter who told me?'

'It matters. P. V. told me himself he wanted to talk to you about it. He ain't got it all set yet.'

'You're lying, just to make me feel better.'

'No, I ain't. I tell you, P. V. is going to talk to you about it.'

She laughed bitterly. 'Oh, sure, after the first showing. He'll ask me how I liked it.'

He called to the waiter and ordered a bottle of wine. They had had three rounds of whisky, and his head was already fuddled, but he wanted time. Sure, Gloria would feel badly about this. And it needn't have happened. That was the pity of it. Vandenberg had meant to have her in it. He had told him so. But . . . how can you have someone in a television programme when you know she might fall flat on her face in the middle of a take?

Gloria picked up her glass of wine, staring into the ruby richness of it, her mouth bitter and her eyes very far away.

'Louis was planning a T.V. programme. Just before he sold out. He had it all worked out—we worked it out together. It was going to be a very feminine thing—a play that women would like. And I was to introduce it. We had it all worked out, Harry.'

'How's the crab-meat, Gloria? You ain't eating it.'

'Fine, Harry. Very good. Harry—remember how we used to come here then? If Louis were alive and were working over the programme, now, we'd come here. You and I. The way we always did.'

'You should of had the steak. Boy, do they know how to cook a steak here.'

'The first play was to have been specially commissioned. He wanted to get the Lunts for it. I told him he couldn't get them, but you know Louis. "If I want them, baby, I'll get them. What do you think this is—a kid's show? We're going to make it something. You and me." '

Harry took a long drink and chewed on his steak. He tried to sound matter-of-fact and simply succeeded in sounding like Harry trying to sound matter-of-fact.

'It's going to be a quiz show.'

'What do we want with a quiz show? That's not for women.' She spoke vehemently.

He shrugged non-committally. 'Agency seems to think it'll be good. Quiz shows go over big. Look at Werkmans.'

'Werkmans! So now we copy our junior competitors. We never used to copy. When Louis was alive we always led.'

Harry refrained from pointing out whither the dead Louis's leadership had taken them. What the hell. Water over the dam now, anyway. And he never had approved of this 'you and me' stuff between Louis and Gloria. Gloria was a good girl and she did a good job, but she weren't no business genius.

Sometimes he thought Louis would have been a lot better off without her help.

That's where Vandenberg was smart. No helpers. No advice. Didn't even ask Harry for advice except on the things that Harry knew about. Take this new T.V. show. Vandenberg knew as much about it as anybody, because even the experts didn't know—they guessed. So he went his own way.

'You and P. V. should get along, honey.' He sat back, pushed away his plate, and let out a belch. 'Boy that was good.'

'We'd never get along. Not in a thousand years.'

'Because he reminds you a little of Louis, maybe?' His face was sly.

'Don't be ridiculous.' She was suddenly preoccupied with her wine.

'Of course,' he went on pointedly, 'he's a gentleman, which Louis wasn't. He ain't got the same accent. But . . . there's a lot of likeness. The same brain. The same quick way of making up his mind. Even looks a lot like him. Gloria, honey, I don't mind working for P. V. I like him. And I think Louis liked him. In spite of the circumstances. I don't see why you can't get along with him.'

When she spoke she sounded as though she were strangling.

'Harry, will you for Christ's sake stop talking about Louis. . . .'

He hunched his shoulder. He felt injured. After all, he was only trying to help her. And what had she been talking about all the evening?

'Okay, kid. Okay. No need to get sore. Let's go somewhere and dance.'

They went dancing. And they drank a lot more. And they stopped feeling mad at each other. They talked about old times again; they laughed and they almost cried over the old times. But the more they drank, the less they cared, and even the unfunny things became funny. Sure, it wasn't such a bad world.

And as the evening wore on, Louis came back into Harry's mind. Louis had never appreciated him. Louis had never done right by Harry. Harry had helped him, got him out of trouble, lent him money, smoothed the way for him with his women. And now here was he, Harry, out dancing with Louis's best girl. And Louis was in his grave.

There was a certain richness about that. Sober, maybe Harry wouldn't have seen it that way. Maybe he would have been shocked at the thoughts in Harry's mind when Harry was drunk. But now the thoughts were rich. Harry held Gloria very, very close, and they did the rumba and the samba and the mambo. They were both very good dancers, even when they were drunk, and they loved to dance. They didn't care if people were laughing at them, the tall dark woman and the short balding man.

Finally, Harry took her home. She kept telling him what a sonofabitch Paul Vandenberg was and how she wouldn't want to touch him with a ten-foot pole, and Harry nodded and smiled and didn't listen.

And that night, for the first and last time, Harry forgot that Gloria was too tall.

XVII

GLORIA's apartment was unexpected. It was over an antique shop on Twenty-third Street, just east of Fourth Avenue, and you entered it by a rickety, dimly lit staircase that suggested furtive things. And then you rang Gloria's bell, and a new world opened before your eyes.

A lot of people wondered why Gloria had never moved into a more fashionable quarter when Vermeyer looked upon her and found what he saw good. But perhaps it was because of Vermeyer that she stayed.

In the beginning, the sprawling, inexpensive apartment had been a challenge and an opportunity; it had given her the space she needed to create something beautiful, a little part of the world she coveted, out of her then modest salary. And as her fortunes improved and money flowed more easily, it still gave her freedom that a more expensive location would have denied her. She bought alabaster lamps from Italy, Persian carpets, antique chairs that were flawless in the elegance of their line. The four rooms began to take on a particular aura. From being a convenience, a place to be apologized for and explained, her home began to be unique. It was 'Gloria's place', words that were spoken with a certain air of wonder and possibly envy. It became so much a part of her that she could not bear to give it up in favour of a more conventional and fashionable address.

And then, undeniably, it was convenient to Louis. No one ever expected to find him in such surroundings. It was a sure refuge where he could evade the world. And if he had by chance run into someone he knew (which never happened), there would have been a ready excuse: it was a business location; some small-time former friend in any one of a dozen trades might be around there.

Sam Woodstock, Gloria's guest for the evening, let his eyes rove with unabashed curiosity and pleasure. He loved her apartment. It was the sort of home he himself would like.

He didn't care a hoot for the insalubrious neighbourhood. The very unexpectedness of the place added to its charm in his eyes. And he didn't need to be told the value of the paintings on the walls or the carpets on the floor. This was style. This was a way of living that had almost gone out.

'Gloria, I'm a bore if you like, but I still can't get over it. This place. It's like—some of the places I saw in Italy. Wonderful homes. Good. Old. Different. And you've made it all.'

'Thank you.' She was pouring coffee. It was strong, café espresso, because she knew he liked it. She was a superb hostess.

Sam had taken to dropping in on her lately, and sometimes they went to a show together. She liked him. There was no romance between them, and he always knew when to go home, and she liked that too. Particularly now she valued that, because she realized with a shock that since she started drinking so heavily she frequently didn't know when it was time for someone to go home. And so she valued highly a guest who knew when to say: 'Okay, sweetheart, you need your beauty sleep. I'll see myself out.'

It was not only his natural good manners that made Sam so chivalrous. He liked Gloria, and he found her company increasingly rewarding in the perplexities of his position with Vermeyers, but also he was afraid of her. He recognized that she was the sort of woman who could spell trouble. Sammy boy, stay away from her, he told himself. Just far enough away. She's too rich for your blood.

But surprisingly she was a good pal.

They had been talking shop tonight. He stirred his coffee with a preoccupied air.

'Gloria, what I don't see in this business is what makes it go. It's so damn easy. And yet it works.'

'How complicated can you make a lipstick?'

'It isn't only the commodity angle—sure, a lipstick is simple, but so is a shirt. You don't get millions out of selling a shirt.'

She yawned. She didn't particularly like to talk shop, save with Harry.

'My dear, there's no sex appeal in a shirt. In spite of the Arrow ads. But make-up . . . You're trading on a woman's

[154]

desire for romance. That's the difference. So she spends a dollar for something that might cost twenty cents to make. Or less. And she thinks she's getting a bargain.'

'But . . . why do they hire someone like me? I'm a lawyer. I know my work. Here . . . Okay, we get a few claims. We have a small amount of patent and registration stuff—which I don't handle. Maybe once in a great while I write a couple of letters. What does it add up to?'

'You mean, where's your future.'

'Right. You bet your sweet life I mean where's my future.'

'If you're smart you'll have a future. If you go with the tide.'

He knew he was boring her. But he had to get it off his chest. He felt insecure. It was a new feeling for him, and he didn't like it, and she was the only one in the whole outfit close enough to be a confidante.

'Gloria, I can't go with the tide, if by that you mean boot-licking and loafing. Okay, I suppose I should. I should be pleased to run errands for Sarnoff and be treated by him like the kid who delivers his papers in the morning. But that wasn't what I was trained for. I don't think Vandenberg should have hired me for that.'

'What makes you think Vandenberg hired you? Did he interview you?'

She had the manner of someone who knew more than she admitted, a certain air of suppressed superiority. He was puzzled.

'No. But I thought—it was pretty obvious. . . .'

'Sam, Gene Pollovic hired you. And Gene Pollovic doesn't like Harry. Does that add up?'

She was patient, but beginning to be a little irritated. He stared at her blankly.

'But I thought—it had to be Vandenberg. Sarnoff is so careful. . . .'

She smiled absently. She was wondering whether it would be impolite to go into the kitchen and fetch a bottle. No, she'd better wait. He was too wound up. Poor little Sam.

'Harry would be careful. That's why he lasts. He'd figure

it might just be Pollovic being a two-timer. Or it might be P. V. So he'd play it safe. Right now I think he's probably figured it was just a game of Pollovic's that didn't pay off. That's why he's being rougher on you.'

Sam still could not quite accept this. It was too bitter a blow to his vanity. To be set there by Vandenberg to find out what was really humming—that made sense. That was more or less what Pollovic had said.

More or less. And Sam suddenly saw why Pollovic had stressed the need for confidentiality. The sonofabitch. The dirty sonofabitch.

'But, Gloria—I gave up a law practice. . . .'

'Pollovic didn't guarantee you anything, did he?'

'No. . . . But he talked of the chances—the future opportunities. He talked of a thirty-thousand-a-year job, in the very near future. And anyway . . .' swinging round again to his disbelief: 'How do *you* know? What makes you so sure?'

She laughed. 'Sammy boy, men talk an awful lot. When they've an admiring audience. And when the man is drinking and the woman is drinking, they talk even more.'

He stared at her with sudden intensity. He spoke slowly. 'Yes. I guess you see an awful lot of men.'

Her eyes were veiled. She leaned her head back, exhaling slowly as she let the cigarette he had just lit for her dangle from her beautiful, long-fingered hands. They were the most photographed hands in the nation, according to one magazine ad.

'Yes, Sam. I see a lot of men. And you know, I get so goddamned sick of them. Sick of listening to their troubles. You know, a woman gets to an age sometimes when she just wishes she had a girl friend. Men just aren't any good to her then. She needs a woman friend. I need one. And there isn't anyone. Women don't like me. And I know it's my own fault and there isn't a damn thing I can do about it.'

Bet it's true, he thought. Career woman. As my revered boss would say, horseshit. But this business about Pollovic . . . It could be true. That would account for the fact that Vandenberg has never sent for me, never given me the slightest sign. But Pollovic led me to suppose I was a personal suggestion of P. V. The dirty, low-down sonofabitch.

'Gloria, that's downright dirty. It's—it's unfair. It's not ethical.'

He found it difficult to express himself sufficiently. She was not really listening.

'I used to think so many things were unethical when I came into this business. The way it's so hard to get promotion if you're a woman. You have to be nice to people. Pollovic never liked me because I wouldn't be nice to him. Then Louis altered all that. And Pollovic kissed my feet. Still does. Still treats me as if I were special. But I don't trust him. Only a fool trusts Pollovic.'

Sam was pacing up and down.

'If Pollovic was just hoping I'd learn the job from Sarnoff so that he could bounce him, he's crazy. Nobody bounces Sarnoff. Sarnoff's smart. He keeps you guessing. All the time I've been there I've run errands for him, I've entertained visiting firemen for him, I've driven him here there and everywhere—I've done everything except get to know just what he *does*. What does he do, Gloria? What *is* Sarnoff's job?'

She started at being addressed. She had been lost in thought. But she caught the last question.

'Being chief trouble-shooter. Oh, it's easy now, but it used not to be. If someone was stealing things from the plant—it was his job to find out who was the inside man, and he always did. If there was a strike, he had to iron it out. If there was trouble with the police—you know, fire regulations or the rest of it—he had to fix it. Any trouble. So long as he never bothered Louis asking how. And he didn't. I could tell you things. . . . But what the hell.'

'What sort of things?' He was sitting down again now, watching her, eagerly.

To her, his eagerness was pathetic. Poor sucker. She wished she'd got that drink. She was awful dry, and the wine with her dinner had simply made her want something more.

'Louis was always in trouble with women. His first wife started to blackmail him once he was on the upgrade. They were all like that—the women he knew in the early days.' Something different had come into her face, a hard, inward-turned intensity. She sighed, rubbed her eyes with her hand

once, then went on: 'This one—I think her name was Rose—
I really forget. Well, she was bleeding him white. He didn't
tell Harry at first. But when he did—Harry fixed it.'

'How?' asked Sam naïvely.

'Oh, he went up to see her. Roughed her up a little and
roughed her boy friend up a lot more. They never gave any
trouble after that.'

Boy, what a bunch, he thought. She takes it so calmly. To
look at them now—those plush offices. The ads. P. V. so very
dignified.

He suddenly wondered: Does P. V. know what went into
the making of it all? Sure. He'd have to. Well, what do you
know.

'Guess I'm just a boy from the country.'

She was on her feet now, and she went swiftly through to
the kitchen before he could forestall her with another question.
When she came back and had poured them each a stiff drink,
she asked slowly:

'Sam, do you get lonely? Living alone, I mean.'

'Hell, I don't live alone. I have my mother with me and my
sister and her husband and their kids and my younger brother.'

'You're lucky. It's so lonely, being alone. You get in and
you shut the door, and you know: No more conversation.
No one to talk to, even about the weather. Until tomorrow
after breakfast. Unless you're lucky and someone drops in.
And that makes you do things you wouldn't do, otherwise.'

'I can't get over that Pollovic,' he said doggedly, taking a
big gulp of the rye she had poured and staring into the glass.
'It's downright dishonest. To take a guy away from a law
practice. To tell him he's going to act as House Counsel. And
the bastard knows all the time that the outside firm of attorneys
get all the real work. I'm just to be a stooge.'

'Sam, know what they did to me? Louis always said we
would go into T.V., and he and I would work out a programme
together. We *were* working on it. Before he—died. And now
they've gone ahead. They've lined up a programme. They've
got it all arranged—and didn't even tell me about it. How do
you like that?'

'But a law practice is something, Gloria—I mean, you just
[158]

don't build it overnight. I can't give this job up like anyone else can—like Ziggie, for instance. She'd get a job anywhere. But I have to wait—build up my practice again. Start in all over. If this is all they mean me to do—it's criminal.'

She was on her second drink, and she looked at the level in the bottle. Half. She'd better go easy. It was the last bottle. Sam might have brought one with him. He'd been round to dinner often enough, now, but he never brought a bottle. Flowers. Who wanted flowers? She always ordered her own, anyway. So they went with the apartment.

She looked at her hand as it held the glass, and it was not steady. Bitterly, she reflected: Maybe he was afraid that would show. Sure, T.V. shows everything. The circles under your eyes and the shaking hand. Didn't he know I'd even go on the wagon for that? For a programme of my own—oh, God, what wouldn't I have done for that.

He could have told me. Given me a chance. Things shouldn't just spring up on you like that. I thought he was just bluffing when he said he had something he wanted to work on with me. And now perhaps he wasn't. Perhaps it was the programme. And I spoilt it all. Spoilt it by getting drunk at Harry's party.

Suddenly, fiercely, she wanted Sam to be gone. Sam was no use. He came to her just to pump her for information and because Ziggie wouldn't have him, she knew. Sure, Gloria knew all the things that made men come to her. And she despised the bunch of them.

All save Harry. Harry was kind, even if he was rough. And then she coloured.

She wished she could remember more about what had happened after they left Tony Pastor's.

Usually, Sam did her good. They played records and laughed and talked of books, plays—all the things she had forgotten to do since she became a part of The House of Vermeyer. But this night had been different. They had talked too much of Vermeyers. When he had gone, she was keyed up, irritable, restless. It was a dangerous mood. It was the mood that made her empty a bottle, if she had one. But tonight she didn't have one.

She took a bath, slowly, trying to relax in the perfumed heat. But although her body was tired and her head buzzing, she knew she would not sleep if she went to bed. That was the real devil that sat on her shoulder. If she could sleep, nothing would be quite as desperate as it was.

The hardest part of her present life was her knowledge that all of her troubles stemmed from her own acts. Gloria couldn't shut her eyes, as some people would have done, and say: I'm a victim of circumstances. Why did this happen to me?

Instead, a small cold voice inside her head was always telling her: It's your own fault. When Louis first made love to you, you should have refused him. Even after that first time, you could have walked away. That first time perhaps it wasn't really your fault, but afterwards it was. You could have left Vermeyers.

As she lay in the bath, head against the hard tile wall, eyes half-closed, her limbs limp, she thought of that first time. She was twenty-five. Six years ago. Six long years. Five of them had been wonderful. And the sixth ... Hell. Just that. Simply and coldly. The nagging loneliness, the thoughts that kept her awake at night, the memories that wouldn't be put into a box. Hell isn't eternal fire or the lash of scorpions; hell is the remembrance of a happiness gone for ever.

Twenty-five. The 'Violets for Madame' promotion. I wore a little flat hat covered with violets, with swathes of pale mauve tulle framing my face. My photograph was in *Life* in colour and *Vogue* called me 'the girl that Romney should have painted'. That was the year we broke in every fashion magazine across the country, simultaneously, with a full-page picture of me—nothing else. No copy. Just me in a chic suit sitting on a marble bench in the square before the Plaza. And the letters rolled in. So many letters, asking what it was all about.

Violets for Madame. . . .

And before the success of it all was known, I was sick. Tired. Overworked. Too many hours of posing in a cold November wind, wearing only a light spring suit. I caught a chill. And Louis was so sweet. He sent violets to my apartment. Violets for Madame. If he hadn't got worried when I didn't call the office and he found no one had been to see me, it probably would never have happened.

I'll always remember the way he came in, that first time. The surprise on his face—almost disgust, that I should live in such a place. And then . . . the wonder. The relief. He had been afraid that I might have the wrong setting. Oh yes, Louis, you collected women as a dealer collects rings. Your taste became more exacting as you climbed the ladder. And that first day when you came here, you knew what was happening to us—what you would make happen. I didn't. I was so naïve.

Louis, I loved you. I loved your dark, intense eyes. I loved your way of smiling. I loved your hands that were always gentle. You knew so much about women. You knew how to make me love you. And then, no doubt, you went away, and laughed, and did the same thing with someone else.

You went out, that first time you came here, and bought chicken at the delicatessen. You bought wine, and made me drink a little. I thought it was just kindness, just because you were ashamed that no one from the office had been to see me. I was really sick. And you knew. You knew what I felt like. You made me feel wanted again.

When you went away, and promised to come back the next day, I just lived for that time when you would be sitting beside my bed again, telling me the gossip of the office and making me laugh. You weren't all bad, Louis. You were kind, sometimes.

But I got well. Influenza doesn't always last long enough. You brought me a new house-coat—a lovely velvet thing, violet-coloured because of the promotion. I still have it, somewhere. And we lit a fire in my funny old fireplace—it was cold, that spring. We sat on the rug, feeding sticks to the flames, and there—it was there you made love to me, Louis. The first time anyone had ever made love to me.

The bathwater was getting cold. She shivered. Slowly she climbed out of the bath, dried herself and showered on the perfumed bath cream and powder that bore the label, 'House of Vermeyer'. That subtle perfume always pervaded her apartment. It made you think of spring evenings, when the night sky was not quite black but deep blue velvet, and the blossom trees were laden.

For a long time she lay wakeful. It was always the same. If she sat in a chair, trying to read, she dozed, and if she took a bath she became drowsy. For a little while. But the mere act of getting into bed, putting out the light and laying her head down on the pillow seemed to chase away the drowsiness. As though the pillow were something inimical, contained some secret power to shiver her into full wakefulness. And then the tossing began.

First one side, then the other. Her pillow was too hard. But if she threw it away and brought a softer one, her head seemed to be sinking down, down, down, into the bottomless depths of nightmare.

The window was open. Perhaps the street noises were distracting her. But they had never distracted her a year ago. Close the window. See if that is better. Then she stifled.

Put on the light again. Where's the book? Read, read. Read till the drowsiness returns. But the lines of print danced before her aching eyes, the effort of concentration spurred her into even greater wakefulness.

Mother of God, she prayed, take this curse from me. I have sinned. Because I have sinned, I can't sleep. Let me sleep. Please let me sleep.

She could not go to confession. Perhaps if she could she might sleep again. But she had renounced her church for Louis, and now she could not regain it. Something had happened to her. I don't believe in all that, she told herself. It's superstition. But that was in the daylight hours. By day, it was superstition, meaningless mumbo-jumbo. At night she prayed, desperately.

In one of these wakeful hours, she thought: I'll go to P. V. I'll tell him what's wrong. That I can't sleep. He was kind, before. Maybe he'll understand. Perhaps a doctor could help me. Even a psychiatrist. Yes, yes, I'll go to a psychiatrist. I'll ask P. V. to help me.

When she finally slept, the morning sky was showing above the roof-tops, and the trucks were on their noisy way about the city. And she dreamed as she slept, of Louis. They were together again in her apartment and he had brought her the violet robe. She felt again the surprising tenderness of his short, stubby-fingered hands.

But it was not Louis. It was Vandenberg, and she called him Paul. When she finally awoke the dream was forgotten, but she awakened with a sense of discovery in her mind, that realization: If I could remember, I would understand something very important. But she could not remember.

XVIII

THE television programme was a success. From the first, much-ballyhooed evening, that was abundantly clear. The long conferences, the tussles with the agency who had thought they knew best, the many weary hours Vandenberg had spent watching other shows—all had paid off. The House of Vermeyer had done it again. Tops in the field, it was tops too in this—the newest field of advertisement. Television had been the only hurdle Vermeyers hadn't attempted, and now they had gone smoothly, effortlessly over the top.

There was nothing new about a quiz show, but there was something distinctly new about the size of the prizes. A hundred-thousand-dollar top. And that still wasn't all. People vied to be called to the show because of the prize money, but it was showmanship that would make people tune in. After the first night's reports, it was obvious that showmanship was there.

Vandenberg had hired Morton Hornby, veteran television producer, to put the show together. And Vandenberg had to admit that in the points where they had differed and he had let Hornby have his way he had no cause for dissatisfaction. Morton knew what made entertainment.

The real difference was in the gimmick. Every show had to have a gimmick. No one would stay tuned in otherwise, because there were too many shows, all much the same. The quiz was good, with progressively harder questions as the prize money went up, and the contestants had a fair chance of winning at least a sizeable sum. But that was mere background. The gimmick was that at some given moment (you never knew when) the lights went out. Everything stopped and one of the husband-and-wife contestants (they had to be husband and wife according to the rules of the show) had to start talking, instantly. They chose, at the beginning of the show, which was to be the one to talk, and the subject was always the same: One partner had to talk, fast, without pause, about the other.

If they faltered, they forfeited the prize money they had hitherto acquired.

The results on that first showing were hilarious. Even Vandenberg, sitting tensely in his own apartment watching it, had laughed. It was funny what people would do for money. That woman had talked. And when you talk fast, like that, without thinking, the things you say. . . .

Now, of course, the question would be: Could they keep it up? Would they always strike it as rich as they had with that big, bosomy redhead? Whenever he thought of her, P. V. laughed again. He loved her. Oh Lord, how he loved her. She had made his show. They couldn't expect as much luck each time. But they would be careful in their selections. Just so long as they were genuine, hardworking, honest couples. Leave the desire for the prize money to do the rest.

The night after the first show, Ziggie and Paul were dining out. It was partly a celebration, and partly the resumption of an evening ritual which had already become a habit, interrupted briefly during the past week because of the demands of the forthcoming television programme.

Paul took her to a Bavarian restaurant in the East Sixties, where the food was superb and the atmosphere quietly charming. An old man played folk songs and traditional airs on a zither. There were candles on the table, and the room was shadowy enough for it to be difficult to recognize the diners at a neighbouring table. It was shadowy enough to hold hands and be youthfully, idiotically romantic, and Vandenberg found himself holding Ziggie's hand.

The past month had sped by swiftly. It was just a month since they had taken the ferry-boat ride. He could scarcely believe that it was indeed he who had taken part in it. It seemed to be an interlude from another and different life, as did this whole episode. Staring now at Sigrid Anderson's face in the pale glow of the candle-light, he thought: She is beautiful. More beautiful than any woman I have ever known. And even as he thought it, he knew that her beauty was in himself, in his tenderness for her, not in her face. He was in love with her.

'What are you thinking?' she asked him.

[165]

'That you are beautiful.'

'Yes, please say it—even though it's not true.'

'It is true.'

'Now I know why poets always sing of beautiful women. They love them, and so for them they are lovely.'

'Wise little Sigrid. I should always call you that, not Ziggie.'

'I don't mind Ziggie, when you say it.'

She had changed in the intervening weeks. She was more sure of herself. The outward poise that had been a garment had become part of herself. There was about her a quality of happiness that transformed her.

'It's been a month,' he said softly.

'A month and two days.'

'You count even the days?'

'Yes. I count even the hours. It was—almost midnight.'

'No regrets?'

'No.'

'Ziggie—you said that night you didn't know me. Do you know me now?'

She hesitated. 'I don't know. I think so.'

'There may be times when I shall surprise you. You may not like it.'

'I love you, Paul. I'm not asking questions. I don't want to ask questions.'

'You haven't even asked—if I want to marry you.'

'No. It doesn't seem important.'

'To a girl like you it must be important. You were brought up a certain way.'

'Yes. But I have to live my own life. Before I met you— this would have seemed impossible. It would have seemed wrong. Now . . . it's all right. It's the thing I have to do. That's all.'

He thought of Gloria. There was a difference here. Perhaps Gloria had never been able to say: It's all right. It's the thing I have to do. What made the difference? What was it about this girl that made him feel safe? That there would be no complications?

Gropingly, trying to put what he felt for her into words, he came up with a picture. Ziggie in a house somewhere, a house with children and dogs. And a piano.

He had always thought about a piano in a big room, when he was younger. He didn't know why it seemed so important. He loved to play, but it was more than that. It was part of something that he wanted. It somehow symbolized something he had striven for and never found, that mental picture of a room where a woman listened while he played.

'I might . . . bring you unhappiness,' he said abruptly.

'Yes. You probably will. It doesn't matter.'

'What does matter?'

'That—that this happened. You see, I always wondered— if it were real. If—falling in love really did happen.' She spoke hesitantly, feeling half-ashamed of what must seem to him to be mere schoolgirl foolishness. 'I've met so many nice, dull young men. I've seen my girl friends get married, be very happy—all wrapped up in men I thought insufferably boring. Mother wanted me to get married. But I couldn't picture myself married to anyone I knew. I couldn't face *living* with any of them. You know, not only going to bed, but all the rest. Seeing them over the breakfast table, looking after their underwear. And I'm twenty-six. I thought—it might never happen. That I might be immune. I was afraid—of ending up alone.'

She had never admitted that. Not to Sharon, not even to herself. But as she thought of the past weeks, looked back with astonishment on her own lack of scruple, she knew it was true. She had been lonely. She had been more afraid of continuing to be alone. What had restrained her with other men had not been virtue, as it would be nice to suppose, or discretion, as Sharon undoubtedly thought. It was that fear—the fear of wasting herself, and finding the real thing afterwards when it was too late. Because if you never found the real thing, or had tied yourself to someone who didn't matter, then you were for ever and utterly alone.

Nothing can take this away from me, she kept telling herself. No matter what happens. Nothing can take it away.

Her eyes were luminous, her mouth trembling. He knew she was near to tears, although he did not guess the reason.

[167]

Emotional, he thought. Young and clean and fresh. With it came another thought: With her it would be different. It might work.

But immediately he mocked himself: It didn't work with the others. All right, this isn't the same. *She* is different. But what have I to offer her? I'm prematurely old, burnt-out, sick. I can give her a few years, perhaps, and money. What does money mean to her? She didn't give herself to me for money. She hasn't even held out—to see if I would marry her first.

Vandenberg knew all the tricks of well brought-up young women. He was infinitely understanding as to the inner workings of propriety. There is more virtue in kindness than in chastity, he thought.

Something sombre and bitter was back in his face, and she reached out her hands and seized one of his as it rested on the checked tablecloth.

'Paul. Don't ask questions. Don't probe. We have this. We have each other. Don't look beyond that.'

We can't look beyond it, she thought. There is just the present. He has so little time left. I have found him when it is almost too late.

It was a driving, constant, insistent pain within her, that thought, the sense of time slipping through her fingers. The memory of the attack which she had seen haunted her now. She remembered the mocking words he had uttered then: 'If I'm careful, I'll make my half-century. It's enough.' Oh no, dear God, it's not enough. I want to marry him. I want to have his children, to have long years with him.

But there was no time for that. She knew it. And she shut her eyes to what she wanted, and took what was offered instead.

'My mother died when I was seventeen,' he said. 'I suppose I've never had any normal home life. We were very close. She was bitterly unhappy—I suppose that's why she turned to me so much.'

'You have a son, don't you, Paul?'

'Yes.' Again the sombre expression clouded his face. 'He doesn't mean much to me. You'll have to meet him. Perhaps you could do something with him. I've often thought—he

[168]

needs a woman. Boys need a woman more than most people realize. There has to be someone—to idealize.'

'I was lucky. Both my parents are darlings.'

'That's why you are so blessedly normal, my dear.'

But she was thinking: They *are* darlings. They've always understood, even when I wanted to leave home. But would they understand this? She shrank from that. Well, if they knew everything, she could make them understand.

He said, as though it were an afterthought:

'They wouldn't like this—this business between you and me.'

'It's my life,' she said again, almost fiercely. 'I'm like my grandmother, Paul. People didn't like what she did, either, but she had to do it.'

'What did she do?'

'She left her home in Sweden, came out here on an immigrant ship. She worked her way across the States. She was —anything. Waitress, farm girl, housekeeper. Her people were good, respectable people. They thought it was shocking.'

'And they were wrong.'

'Yes. We all know—whether what we are doing is right. That's all we can go by.'

He liked her best when she had that fierce, stubborn look on her face. Yes, he could believe she came from pioneer stock.

'Ziggie,' he said, again at a tangent, 'I'm a Jew. I suppose you're a Protestant.'

She was surprised at the remark. She knew, as did anyone who knew him at all, that he was Jewish.

'Yes.'

'Does it make any difference?'

For answer she felt for his hand again, and he seized her fingers. She said simply:

'How could it? What have our religions to do with—loving each other?'

He wondered himself why he had thought of it. He did not practise his religion. He hadn't been to the Synagogue in years. Old ties, old bonds, old loyalties, he thought. How deeply they are rooted. But she's right. There's no conflict. Not for either of us.

He felt a sudden and urgent desire to talk to her. Not small

[169]

talk, not the idle things a man said to a woman he had taken out for an evening. It seemed to him imperative that she know him. All about him. All about his father, about his marriages.

She hero-worships me, he thought. She puts me on a pedestal, because I've made money. Because, in this cock-eyed world we live in, sixty million dollars is a symbol of success, not failure.

Only a failure makes money—that much money. He makes it to atone for the other things he hasn't got. Happiness. Love. Talent.

If I could play the piano as I wanted to play it, as my mother wanted me to play it, I'd be poor. I'd be playing for audiences, instead of for myself, at night, when I'm tired and angry.

If I even had been able to make a go of marriage, it would be different. I'd be a successful father, instead of someone who doesn't know how to talk to his child. It's not the boy's fault, it's mine.

Paul Vandenberg, you're a failure. You've failed at everything you've ever tried in your life, except this one sordid thing. You know how to make money. You are your father's son.

'Let's go,' he said.

She was used to his swift changes of mood. Already she knew that sometimes in the middle of dessert, over a drink, at a recital which had just begun—he would touch her hand, look about him for the waiter or gather up his coat, and say brusquely always the same simple words: Let's go. And without question she arose and went with him, holding his arm, saying nothing, waiting for the mood to pass or for him to tell her what chance word or thought had banished the light from his face.

They left the shabby little restaurant which was yet very exclusive, and walked slowly down the street towards the river. When they reached the water they turned uptown, and walked on until they came to an elevated, railed look-out. There they climbed the steps and stopped, and he rested his arms upon the railing, looking down into the swirling black waters of the East River.

'It goes towards Hellgate,' he said.

'Yes. It's so swift—and so evil.'

[170]

'I never think of the river as evil. It's a refuge.'

She shivered, in spite of the warmth of the night. His face was rapt as he stared downwards.

He sighed. Then, turning to her, as though to break the spell cast by the dark water, he half smiled.

'Ziggie. Do you know why I brought you here?'

'Because you like the river?'

'No. Because I didn't want to propose to you in a public place.'

The blood pounded in her ears, and she felt faint. This is idiotic, she thought. She put her hands on the cool rail to steady herself.

He was still smiling, looking down into her face. And in the same light, amused tone he asked her:

'Well, Ziggie, will you marry me?'

She slid her arms about him, beneath his coat, brushing her cheek against his throat. She whispered, stumblingly:

'Oh, Paul. . . . Of course. I love you, I love you. . . .'

He held her pressed very tightly against him, the warm pulsing touch of her body at once an excitement and a solace. It may be mad, he thought, but it is right. We'll have—a little while.

'Ziggie—I can't offer much to a young wife. I have to be careful. I may not have long——'

She put her hand over his mouth.

'Don't talk about it. Don't ever talk about it. We have each other, we *will* have each other. That is all that matters.'

And she pulled his head down and kissed him, repeatedly, her eyes closed and her cheeks wet with tears. For all his experience, no woman had ever kissed him like that. He felt intoxicated.

Finally, he broke away from her.

'Let's find a cab.'

In the cab, she leant gently against him, and they were both very much at peace. And never with any other woman had he known the sense of harmony that he found with this girl. At first, it had been simply a warmth in her that pleased him, an unexpected womanliness that didn't fit with his idea of a career girl. But it had grown. In a short month he had seen it

[171]

blossom into full maturity. She anticipated his mood and suited herself to it. It was as though she said to the world: Stay away from him. This is my love and it shall be his protection. What he wants he shall have.

He knew it was not wise to take her back to his apartment. Yet from the first he had fought against taking her to a hotel. There seemed something unbearably squalid about the deception that it involved. On that first evening, an intuitive regard for her feelings had prompted him to take her to his own place, and now it seemed right and natural. Well, they would be married as quickly as possible. Now that the decision was made, he was anxious to hasten their marriage.

He was pouring a glass of wine for her when the telephone rang. Frowning a little, he glanced towards her as he moved to answer it. She was sitting in an armchair, completely relaxed and smiling happily. The word 'uncomplicated' recurred to him. Yes, that was it. A part of it. And the grace of her posture struck him. She never made a gauche or awkward movement. In other circumstances, what a wife she would have made. A lover, a hostess. A mother, God willing.

'Hullo. Oh, yes, I forgot to stop by the desk. All right. Anyone else? Thank you.'

He hung up, the frown deepening.

'Something wrong?' she asked.

'I don't know. Gloria Vernon called three times while I was out. I remember now. She wanted to see me yesterday. It slipped my mind because of the programme.'

It was a small knot of worry, and also a bore. He found the whole problem of Gloria Vernon tiresome. He had tried to help her, but he was not a particularly patient man. He had little use for someone who refused to help herself.

The name cut across her happiness like a knife. Gloria Vernon and Louis Vermeyer. Ziggie Anderson and Paul Vandenberg. Yes, she had thought about that a lot in the past month. Well, put it away. Put it away where he won't see it.

But he had seen it. He saw it because he too had thought of the similarity. He remembered what he had felt when he first met Gloria Vernon. He had thought Louis Vermeyer a fool to become involved with a woman of his own organization.

[172]

Well, it was different. He was free, and Ziggie would be his wife as soon as he could make her his wife.

He went across to her, swiftly, dropping down on his knees beside her chair, pulling her to him.

'Ziggie . . . It isn't the same. Stop thinking about it.'

She was thinking, as she clung to him: We all do the same things. We look down on other people, and then it happens to us. And we all think: This is different.

At that moment the doorbell rang. He swore.

'Probably my mail. They send it up if I forget to stop by for it. Go into my room, Ziggie.'

She nodded, and stood up. There were tears in her eyes, and it bothered him. Tears always bothered him; they marred a woman's face too much.

He watched the door close behind her, and went across the room, preoccupied. He opened the front door and then stood still in astonishment. It was not the page-boy, but Gloria Vernon.

Before he could speak, she blurted out:

'I'm sorry, but I had to come. I knew they were lying. They kept saying you were out. So I didn't ask for you, I just came up. It wasn't fair to do that to me. I have a right to see you. Everyone has a right to appeal. Miss Shaw wouldn't let me see you in the office. It's so easy to keep people away, isn't it, if you're P. V?'

The words rushed out. She was distraught, but sober, he noticed.

'Apparently not,' he replied dryly. He was trying to think his way out of this mess. What in God's name was up now? Reluctantly, he stood back. 'Come in. But I must warn you I can't talk to you now. Forgive me for not calling you back yesterday. I was very busy with the television show.'

'Oh yes. The show. Congratulations. You must be feeling very happy about it.'

He felt embarrassed by her bitterness. She stripped herself by it.

'Miss Vernon, it would be better if you went home now and saw me in the morning. Whatever is wrong can wait until then, I'm sure.'

She was obviously trying to get a hold on herself. She sat down, shivering violently and clasping her hands together. Unthinkingly, he made a move to the sideboard, then checked himself. No, not a drink. He glanced towards the bedroom door. He hoped fervently that Ziggie wouldn't get impatient.

She intercepted the glance.

'Oh—am I interrupting something?'

She did not know why she said it. It had not occurred to her that he might not be alone, but now that it did a malevolence that even she could not understand enveloped her.

He spoke very coldly.

'Miss Vernon, I should appreciate it if you would say whatever you came here to say.'

So that you can go back to whoever is in there, she thought. And all her carefully planned phrases vanished. She hated him. It only mattered that she vent that hatred.

'I'm sorry to be such a nuisance, Mr. Vandenberg. I just wanted to know—why I was fired.'

It was a complete bolt from the blue. He stared at her.

'Fired. . . . I don't understand.'

She laughed.

'You didn't think I'd come here, did you? It was so easy to refuse to see me in the office. And to tell your switchboard to say you were out. Well, this is one time you're not going to get out of listening to what someone thinks of you. You're contemptible, Mr. Vandenberg. Utterly contemptible. You get other people to do your dirty work for you. At least you might have had the decency to tell me yourself.'

That wasn't what she had come here to say. She had meant to ask him *why*. To ask for another chance. To promise to be good. She was terrified at what she was saying. But the words came tumbling out, as though spoken by a stranger. I'll never get another job, she thought. He'll see to that. And in this business, you don't even have to see to it. No one wants one of the top-liners who has slipped. Why am I here? Why don't I say what I came here to say?

He was still standing in the middle of the room, watching her. Gradually her meaning penetrated his awareness. He ceased to wonder if Ziggie might emerge from the inner room.

'You say you have been fired. By whom?'

She stared at him inimically. She had stayed sober tonight because she had to think clearly; she had felt: He will be fair. She had hoped to persuade him to give her another chance. At the back of her mind was the suspicion: Maybe Pollovic had been lying. But now that she was face to face with him, seeing him cool and imperturbable, the very picture of a distinguished gentleman at ease in his own home, she felt herself to be at a disadvantage. To defend herself against him, she conjured up the old formula: But for you, Louis would be alive.

'By Pollovic. Who else handles such chores for you?'

'What reasons did he give you?'

'Oh, he was very specific. You have found me, apparently, an unstable character. I drink too much. I have not—reformed.'

For a moment he did not speak. The effrontery of the Personnel Director amazed him. He had known for a long time that Pollovic was a man who loved his own sense of power. It had not occurred to him, however, that he would exercise it in the matter of anyone so highly placed as the Director of Training, regardless of her record.

He began to be angry. It was a serious enough breach of his own instructions that Gloria Vernon should be fired without consultation with him. But Pollovic had placed him in an invidious position. Vandenberg had been contemplating letting her go; he had come to realize that he was not the man to salvage her. But it had to be done carefully, so that she might start again. It could be arranged. If she knew in advance, if the right introductions were made. . . . There was always a decent way to do things.

He knew Pollovic's way—the Vermeyer way. Five o'clock on the last day of the month you were called in to the Personnel Office and given your pay for the past month. And that was all. It was one of the practices he had been first to prohibit.

'Did he give you any severance pay?'

For the moment he was more interested in the method of the offence than in the offence itself. He had almost forgotten Gloria as a person.

'Oh, yes, I must thank you for your generosity, Mr.

Vandenberg. I was given the princely sum of one month's pay.'

That sonofabitch, he thought. And if she hadn't come to me I would no doubt have been told that she had resigned. Pollovic must feel very sure of himself to take such action. No doubt he felt I had given up on her.

He pondered. He knew it would be useless to tell Gloria that she was not fired by him; she would not believe it. Her visit to his apartment at this unorthodox moment had put him in a position where he was damned whichever way he acted. He could either acquiesce in her dismissal, which was unthinkable under the circumstances, or he could keep her on, which was not in his long-range plans and which would give her a false sense of having triumphed over him. He was too well aware of her enmity for him to suppose she would be grateful for a reprieve.

As he studied her with detachment, he found it easy to see why Gloria Vernon had so many enemies. She was not an easy woman to cope with. So even Pollovic was an enemy. He had bided his time.

'Miss Vernon, will you please go home and try to sleep. In the morning I should like you to come to the office as usual, and come to see me at nine-thirty. We will talk about this then.'

'You mean you won't reconsider?'

'I mean only what I have said. Pollovic did not act on any orders from me.'

She smiled twistedly. 'That is very easy to believe. Are you aware that Gene has always been—very friendly towards me?'

'I'm aware, among other things, that I wouldn't count too much on Eugene Pollovic's friendship. Such friendships have been known to change with—whatever wind is blowing.'

'So that's all you will say?'

'That's all I will say tonight.'

She felt trapped. She felt also an unwilling admiration for him. He wasn't an easy man to push. In a fleeting moment of disloyalty she wondered what Louis would have done in similar circumstances, then she brushed the thought aside. There was no point in comparison.

She stood up, feeling all at once very tired, beaten. To-night she didn't even want a drink. It wouldn't help. She just wanted to crawl into bed, and sleep, and not wake up.

Sleep. Maybe that was the way. If she had enough pills. Trouble was, you never knew how many were enough. She'd tried that once. Just slept for two days and was sick and miserable afterwards. You couldn't be sure.

As she went towards the door, he moved towards her. Something of the blank despair in her face moved him. When she cried he felt only distaste, and drunk she was disgusting. But now she had a dignity and pathos that he had not seen in her before.

'Miss Vernon . . . I'm not an enemy. I told you that once—remember? I wish you would believe it.'

She stopped apathetically, facing the door. Then she glanced back towards him, about to speak, and as she did so her eyes saw something that riveted her attention. Seeing the change in her expression, he looked in the direction in which she was staring.

On a chair by the wall was a large, flat, black handbag, with the initials 'Z. A.' monogrammed in gold. The handbag had been Sarnoff's present to his secretary the previous Christmas and as Gloria looked fully into his face, anger and mockery mingling in her expression, Vandenberg knew that she recognized it.

'Oh, I forgot,' she said, very quietly. 'Among the other things that Mr. Pollovic gave as the reason for my dismissal. . . . Apparently you don't think I have comported myself in a manner fitting to an executive.' Her eyes suddenly blazed at him. 'You goddamned hypocrite.'

With that, she was gone, the door slamming behind her. He stood still, shaking.

He heard a quiet movement behind him. Ziggie had heard the slamming of the front door, and tentatively entered the room. Finally he turned.

'It was Gloria Vernon.'

He went across to the sideboard, finished pouring two glasses of wine and brought them across to where she stood. She sat down, thanked him quietly, and watched. She was frightened by the look on his face.

He drank his wine straight down, standing. Then he set down the empty glass and began pacing slowly up and down the room. After a moment he stopped, facing her.

'Pollovic fired her yesterday. She thought it was my doing. She came here to tell me what she thought of me.'

She felt relieved and also puzzled. So that was all. Why should he take it so seriously?

'Did you tell her you hadn't told him to?'

'Yes. She didn't believe it, of course.'

'If you countermand his action, she will have to.'

'I can't countermand it. Not now.'

'Why?'

She was groping. There was something here she could not follow. And anyway, was it so important? Gloria was a jughead. She should have been canned long ago.

Vandenberg was watching her levelly.

'Gloria saw your handbag on the chair over there. If I countermand Pollovic's decision now, she will consider it—an act of appeasement. I dislike being blackmailed, even by accident.'

Her handbag. Oh, damnation. Why hadn't she thought of picking it up?

She felt that Vandenberg too was asking himself that same question. His tone was icy.

Again she felt frightened. This was a mood in which she had never seen him. She felt that she was in the same room with a stranger.

'Paul . . . I'm sorry.'

'It's not your fault.'

'I should have seen it. The handbag, I mean.'

He passed his hand wearily over his forehead.

'It would have made very little difference. She knew someone was inside. The bag merely—identified you.'

He was pacing again. She began to feel hurt. The magic of the night had gone. This was the night that Paul had proposed to her. Oh, why did this have to happen tonight?

'Paul—were you going to keep her on?'

[178]

'No. She'll never be any use to us. She's got to start again, somewhere else.'

'Then why not—let her go? Help her but—let her go?'

'And have her telling everyone that I fired her because she was unlucky enough to find you and me together?' he said irritably. 'Besides—there's more to it than that. She'd never get another job if I just—threw her out. She's her own worst enemy.'

'But, darling—is that your problem? Doesn't Gloria have to fight her own battles?'

'She became my problem when I took over Vermeyers. You take over a business—you take over the people in it.'

It was her turn to be cold.

'You fired plenty of people when you moved in.'

'Yes—for incompetence. For chiselling. Not for being in an emotional tailspin because of the death of a man who meant—just about everything to her.'

'You're very understanding where Gloria is concerned.'

He stared at her suddenly, his old, penetrating stare. Then he smiled.

'And you are uncharacteristically hard. My dear, she *is* still a very beautiful woman. But I am not interested in her personally.'

She coloured.

'That's more than I can say about Gloria.'

'What do you mean?' He spoke sharply.

She laughed. 'I thought everyone knew it. But I suppose you wouldn't. You've taken Louis Vermeyer's place in Gloria's oh so constant heart.'

His expression was blank. 'You're out of your mind,' he said at last.

She tilted her head, maliciously. 'If you think so, ask Harry Sarnoff. He's a very hard-headed man. And he likes Gloria.'

'Which you don't.'

'That's right. I've never pretended to.'

It hurt him unaccountably, that streak of hardness in her. Oh, Ziggie, Ziggie. Don't be little and feminine about this.

He came over and stroked her head.

'My dear. You can afford to be generous.'

[179]

She sat rigidly, resisting the caress of his hand. When she spoke, he knew she was struggling with tears again.

'Tonight—tonight should have been *ours*. Doesn't it—doesn't it mean anything—to you?'

He smiled, unhappily, over her head. Oh, Ziggie, yes. It means so much. But time doesn't stand still, so that we can celebrate our private happinesses. For someone somewhere it is always the dark, lonely night of the bottomless pit.

He pulled her to her feet, folding her to him, feeling the shudder of her body as she tried to stifle her sobs. He smoothed her hair, protectively.

'Ziggie—first thing in the morning—let's see to the licence.'

'Yes, Paul.'

And she thought: We're going to be married. And it's not at all what I thought it would be. It doesn't feel the way I expected.

She was crying again, and it was not because of Gloria. It was because she knew she had spoilt something. She felt she had failed him.

'Paul . . . Paul, I'm sorry.'

It was merely a whisper near his ear. He smiled again, and whispered back:

'I know. I know, my dear.'

XIX

VANDENBERG had dismissed Ziggie's random remark as
nonsensical, but inevitably it recurred to him. While a
man of less than normal vanity, he was inevitably aware
that women were habitually attracted to him (or, as he was
more likely to put it, attracted to his money). In his present
position there was a certain glamour for a woman working in
his company. He was the mystery man who had come in and
put a tottering business back on to its feet, his was the power of
life and death. These facts gave him a certain morbid fascination for a number of the women who worked for him. But he
would have wagered any sum that Gloria Vernon was not one
of them.

As he drove down to the office early next morning, watching
the back of Jim Mahoney's red, wrinkled neck, he was pondering his dilemma. Ziggie's suggestion had not lessened the com-
plication. While he might ridicule the idea, if it were true it
was one more reason for pitying the girl.

That was his strongest feeling for her, and it still surprised
him. Before it had bordered on contempt, but last night had
changed that. She had been unwise, but she had had a certain
defiant dignity and bravado that he liked. And he admired the
courage of her parting gibe. He might have the power of life
and death over Gloria Vernon, but she was not subdued by it.
He wondered what she might have amounted to had circumstances been different.

Promptly at nine-thirty he called her on the interphone. He
had wondered whether she would be at her desk. She was. She
sounded calm and firm. No tears today, apparently. That was
good. He asked her to come in.

When she entered, the first thing he noticed was that she was
dressed very carefully, in a pale grey dress that suited her
admirably. Her hair and make-up were flawless. She might
have posed for a 'perfect woman executive' ad.

He smiled, and indicated a chair.

'Please sit down.' He flipped the inter-office 'phone lever. 'No calls, please, Miss Shaw.'

Gloria waited for him to speak. She was trembling, in spite of her apparent calm. She had spent a frantic night after leaving Vandenberg's apartment, regretting her insanely personal words. Finally she had risen at five and walked the streets until it was time to go home and bathe and prepare for the interview. And surprisingly, now that what she had dreaded for months had happened, she was ready to meet it with at least outward composure. She knew that she was fired.

He seemed to have difficulty starting the conversation. He stared at her for a long moment and she could not fathom what was in his mind. Instead, she found herself looking away because his eyes disconcerted her.

'Miss Vernon, first I am going to ask you again to believe that Pollovic had no orders from me. That matter will be dealt with. Then I wish you to try to act as though that interview had not taken place.'

Her heart beat wildly. Did he mean she was not fired? But she would not ask him. She waited.

'I have not discussed you in any way with Eugene Pollovic. I thought I had made it clear to him that the hiring and firing of top executive personnel was my own exclusive concern. So you may disregard anything he said to you. It did not come from me.'

There was the faintest suggestion of colour in her cheeks. She was thinking: He's afraid. Because of what I know.

He went on, imperturbably:

'However, for some time now I have been planning to have this talk with you. Pollovic's action has merely hastened it. Put briefly, I don't think you and I can work together. You have—personalized—too many issues.'

Her eyes widened. This was cruel. This was cat and mouse. She began to speak, but he interrupted her gently.

'No. Let me finish. I want you to know all my thinking, before you try to answer any part of it.'

'What I am saying to you now I would have said anyway, regardless of what happened last night. That has nothing to do with it. I want you to know that.

[182]

'You can't be happy here. I realize that. I am not so devoid of imagination that I don't know what it has cost you to go on in the same job, in the same surroundings, talking to the same people—when your own personal loss was so great.

'What I want you to do is this: For your own sake, you have to work, and you have to have work which is congenial and creative. I know it isn't easy to find something which will replace your position here. But I think you can do it. You have a lot of ability. You also have a number of friends.

'You are *not* under notice. Pollovic, for your own private information, will not be with us after today. If it takes a year for you to find what you want, that's all right. I think it would be better for you if it took considerably less. You have my best wishes, and anything I can do to help you I will do. I want you to feel free to come to me at any time, and whatever problems you face I'll try to help you overcome them.'

He finished, and sat watching her. At first, she wanted to sneer or cry. She tried to say to herself: He's buying me off. Because of what I know. Then she looked into his face, and she knew she was deceiving herself. He didn't care what she knew. He wasn't even considering it. Suddenly she knew that he was speaking the simple truth. This was what he would have said, anyway. He was being generous.

And that was the hardest thing of all to bear. You steel your-self for ill-treatment, you prepare to be a martyr. It isn't so difficult. But this magnanimity tore down her defences.

And what did it add up to? She was through, anyway. It was a suspended sentence.

'Thank you, sir.' She spoke very slowly. She didn't know what else to say.

'And Gloria.' (It was the first time he had used her first name.) 'The world isn't against you. If you will only stop fighting it.'

'I know.' She spoke almost in a whisper. She could not bear his kindness.

She rose abruptly. She had made up her mind that she would stay calm and professional. She even mustered a smile.

'Well, I'll get back to my office. Thank you for being so—patient.'

He rose to open the door for her, and as he did so she said impulsively:

'Mr. Vandenberg. I'm sorry—about what I said last night.'

He gave her his slow, wonderful smile. 'We all say such things—some time or another in our lives. I assure you—I haven't thought about it unduly.' He put out his hand. 'Good luck.'

'Thank you,' she said again, and then turned and went quickly out of the room. She had to get away, away from his kind, compassionate eyes.

Oh God, she thought, they say he's hard. If they only knew.

For Vandenberg, it was a strenuous day. The interview with Pollovic was brief and unpleasant. When it was over, and he knew he had nothing more to lose, Pollovic suavely loosed his final barb:

'I'm sorry, sir, if I made a mistake. I realized you had taken over the assets of Louis Vermeyer, but I didn't realize that those assets included Miss Vernon.'

And Vandenberg, outwardly unmoved, thought: You garbage-hunting snake. So that's going to be the story to account for your dismissal.

So grows the legend. You can't win. The few decent things you do sometimes add up to more opprobrium than the evil things that you have to hide away. What the hell.

And then the rest of the day was upon him, with reports on the television show and suggestions for improvements in the next week's programme, plus a routine colour conference for the following spring shade and lunch with the head buyer of the most important California department store.

It was five o'clock before he realized that he had done nothing about a marriage licence. And he had not called Ziggie.

He rang for Miss Shaw.

'Miss Shaw, will you please call Miss Anderson and ask her not to leave without speaking to me. And then shut the door and keep out callers. I want to rest for an hour.'

He was exhausted. Wryly, as he lay down on the smooth leather couch, he thought: What a bridegroom. Poor little Ziggie. You deserve much better.

For Ziggie, too, the day was not easy. It had been late when Paul put her into a taxi for home, and she had slept badly into the bargain. She awoke with a feeling of depression which she could not at first define. Then she remembered that, for the first time, she and Paul had clashed.

It had been an intangible thing, but there had been disharmony between them. No, she thought, I'm no good at pretending; last night I was jealous, and I let him see it. It seemed to her now incredibly foolish. If she were going to be jealous every time Paul came in contact with a good-looking woman, she was in for a miserable time.

So she immersed herself determinedly in work.

The mail was heavy. The usual assortment: complaints from women who were allergic to something; begging letters, asking for contributions for charitable functions; inter-office memoranda; a letter from a woman who had spilt nail enamel on her best bedspread and wanted to sue them for damages because it wouldn't wash off; two letters marked 'Personal', which she did not open, but placed on Sarnoff's desk. (She knew the handwriting of most of his female correspondents; they did not need the 'personal' sign to assure privacy.)

When the telephone rang, something in her stiffened. She expected momentarily that Paul would call to arrange with her about going to the registrar's office. But it was never his voice on the wire.

And when he did not call, the depression of the morning deepened. This should have been so different. After all, he had proposed to her. This should have been the happiest day she had ever known. Instead, she felt only—foreboding. A nagging sense of impending unhappiness. The idiotic thought occurred to her: Perhaps he regretted his proposal. And that was enough to send her frantically back to her chores.

Sam noticed her preoccupation, and wondered. For a long time he had seen nothing of her, save in the office, and lately there had been a reserve about her, even there. She had taken to dashing out of the office sharply at five-thirty, which was unusual in her. There was an air of suppressed excitement about her that she tried unsuccessfully to conceal. But today it

[185]

was not excitement. There was obviously something on her mind. She was edgy.

'Ziggie,' he said finally, 'what's wrong?'

She looked up from a letter she was composing, surprised. 'Nothing, Sam. Why?'

'You don't talk to me any more. And you didn't say good morning.'

His manner was light-hearted and kind at the same time. She looked away.

'Overhung,' she lied. 'I had a heavy date last night.'

'You mean I have a rival?'

'Oh, dozens.'

'That's what I like about you,' he chaffed. 'You're so modest.'

When she went back to her work, he was still watching her. So something *has* happened to her, he thought. Wonder who it is.

And cynically he added: Hope he has plenty of money. Because that little lady surely knows what she wants out of life, and it isn't love in a cottage.

The telephone rang again, but it was only Dr. O'Malley. A patch test on a new product had got itself fouled up. The doctors had turned up at the appointed place to test fifty girls, but the girls were missing. Someone had confused the dates. O'Malley was annoyed.

'Ziggie, I love you, but you know how busy I am. I can't have my doctors running around Manhattan trying to stick patches on non-existent girls!'

'Doctor, I'm very sorry. I don't know what went wrong. Can you hold on? I've got the plant on the private wire now —I'm checking. . . .'

Telephone calls, endless telephone calls. And she heard her own voice giving the correct answers, calling the proper people. And still no word from Paul. Didn't he know that this day was special? Couldn't he find time to call her?

A little after five, Elizabeth Shaw called. Would she please not go home until she had spoken to Mr. Vandenberg; Mr. Vandenberg was resting now but he would call her when he was ready.

And then the sun began to shine again and the birds to sing. A great weight lifted from Ziggie's shoulders. He had just had too busy a day, poor darling. Gaily she told Miss Shaw:

'I'll gladly wait.'

It was after six when he called. Sarnoff and Sam had left. His first word was an apology.

'Ziggie. I'm sorry. I got tied up.'

'It doesn't matter.'

'But we were going to see about the licence.'

'Tomorrow's another day.'

'You're very understanding.'

'Oh, not all the time. I'm sorry too—about last night. I was . . . mean.'

He laughed. His laugh still fascinated her. It had a slow, intimate quality that sent the blood to her cheeks.

'But very human.'

'What did you do?'

'Put it on the basis of an extended notice period. No pressure and all the help I can give.'

'You're good, Paul.'

'That isn't what the world says.'

'The world doesn't know.'

'Why are we wasting time on this telephone when we could be talking personally?'

She laughed delightedly. 'I don't know. Has Miss Shaw gone?'

'Yes. I'm all alone. And you?'

'Ditto. Shall I meet you at the Plaza?'

'Yes. In the lounge. In ten minutes?'

'Okay.'

'And Ziggie . . .'

'Yes, Paul?'

'Would you feel like a drive tonight, and dinner at my home?'

'You mean—Fairfield?'

'Yes. I'd like you to meet Laurie. My boy. Tomorrow's Saturday. If you felt like it you could stay over the weekend.'

She felt that it meant a great deal to him. His boy. There was something heart-breaking about the way he said that. She knew that he did not get along too well with his son. Everyone knew it.

'Paul, I'd love that. I want him to like me.'

'Well. Let's meet in the lounge. And we can stop by your place and pick up what you need.'

As she hung up, she thought: Never mind about the licence. This is more important. He wants me to get along with his son.

They met in the lounge, and they were casual, as they always were, any one of a hundred couples meeting for a dinner date. They had their one drink, and then left. And not until they were in the car, with Mahoney driving them, did he kiss her.

Even then, it was a discreet kiss. But it was enough. She saw the tenderness in his face, a new, gentler expression that had not been there before, and she knew he had no regrets.

And on the long drive, slow because of the heavy traffic, he was thinking the same thing. He had thought himself beyond marriage, too old, too near the end of the road. And now it seemed completely natural to be planning another. It's not like any of the others, he thought. Save for Margot, I was never in love with the other women, and that—that was a twisted love. Now—I think I love this girl. In the real sense of the word. Curious.

She was excited at the thought of seeing his Connecticut home. She had seen photographs of it, and knew it to be quite a showplace. But there was more to this visit than that. It put the seal of respectability on their relationship. She felt that even her parents would see it that way. A bachelor apartment, however much it was home to its owner, was not a place to tell your mother that you had visited. But she could imagine now writing home.

Darlings, she would say, the most wonderful thing has happened. I'm in love with a fabulous man, and we're engaged to be married. Last weekend I went down to his home in the country, and met his son—he's a good bit older than I and has been married before, but don't be worried. You'll love him.

She would not tell them yet who he was. No. Let them meet him first, because inevitably they would know things about him—all the wrong things. Everyone did. And when

[188]

they knew him, it would be different. They *would* love him. They couldn't help it.

The house was beautiful, even beyond her expectations. Although only a few years old, it had an ageless style that blended unobtrusively with the countryside, so that it seemed to have grown there. It was protected by fine old trees, and could be seen only once one had entered the estate. She stood back, before entering, admiring it, and he laughed at her.

'You look for all the world like a real estate man.'

'Darling. . . . It's so perfect. You have to remember, I'm the daughter of a builder!'

'I didn't know.'

'Oh yes, Daddy built nearly all the nicest homes in our neighbourhood. But nothing like this. We don't run to millionaires in St. Paul.'

'Then you must be happy people. Millionaires are a sign of imbalance. Cancers in the economic body.'

She linked her arm through his and together they entered the house. It was typical of him that his home had no name. She had thought that the postal designation, Hunter's Run, was the name of the house, but he explained that it was simply the old name for the site on which he had built, derived from a small stream that traversed it.

'But it should have a name, Paul. A house isn't complete without one.'

'You shall name it,' he told her, 'if you like it enough to live here.'

He said it off-handedly, and she felt almost dizzy. *If* she liked it enough. . . . And, of course, to him it was nothing. Just one more building, a collection of stones and timbers and fabrics that had been put together to suit his whim, and had as rapidly bored him.

After showing her the room that was to be hers for the weekend, he took her into his own den, a smaller room lined with books and panelled in dark oak. It was a room she loved immediately, although she put her finger on its one lack.

'Darling,' she said abruptly, 'do you have a dog?'

'No. I stay here too seldom.'

'But you like them?'

He laughed at her obvious concern. 'Yes. I like them very much.' He brought her a drink and put his arms tenderly around her. He had poured nothing for himself. 'You think such a house should have dogs.'

'Yes. I love dogs. I've always dreamed of—a house like this. With dogs and babies all over the place.'

'We shall have them. All over the place.'

His arms closed tightly, without warning. She let out a little wail.

'Darling—my drink! It's all over you.'

The momentary tension she had not seen as he pressed her to him went out of his face; he laughed and released her.

'Don't worry. I'll change. You may find Laurie somewhere. Roam around and see whatever you want to see.'

She nodded, as he shook the soda from his jacket, and left her. At first she stood still, staring about her at the room, trying to read from it more of the man with whom she was to share her life—for a while.

Oh, damn. If she could forget that. If she could dream all the dreams that every woman dreamed when she was about to be married. But there was always that ghost in the background. A few years. How old was he? Forty-four? And he had talked of living to fifty. If he were careful.

I'll look after him. I'll see that he rests. He *must* be careful. We'll see new doctors. Perhaps if he retired. . . .

She wondered: Could he retire? Was this insatiable hunger for money simply a substitute for happiness? Could he let go the reins now, and just be happy—with her?

For the first time in her life, she felt miserably inadequate. What could she offer? What was she, to take the place of an entire way of life? And yet, if he kept up the pace he now kept up, there would be very little that either of them could look forward to.

She knew the sort of time-table he kept. Vermeyers had claimed pretty much of his time, but there were the other ventures. There were the board meetings and the policy conferences for his other companies; there were the endless business luncheons and dinners. He *had* to let go. She had to make him so happy that he would be glad to retire.

Children, she thought urgently. We'll have children. Right away. He will love them, they will be his interest. Even Laurie means more to him than he realizes. And it will be different, once we are a family.

She left the den and prowled aimlessly through the lower floor. It was all so beautiful it took her breath away. It was also a little awe-inspiring. The living-room was huge, with a grand piano near the window. She thought of the piano in his apartment, and made up her mind: Tonight I shall hear him play. Here there will be time for that.

As though to mock her, the telephone rang. It was answered immediately from somewhere in the house. She wondered: Somebody who wants him for a business conference? Or— a friend . . . ?

There was a clatter of boots on the polished boards of the hall, and she turned to the door just as a boy entered. Her first reaction was that he was the most handsome child she had ever seen, then she thought: but—not like his father. Something too beautiful about him. Almost girlish.

'Hello,' she said, smiling.

'Good evening,' he answered, very politely. 'I'm Laurie. My father told me to find you here.'

'That was nice of him. Come in and keep me company.'

He was painfully shy. She sat down on the rug before the big fireplace. It seemed to disconcert him.

'Why do you sit on the floor?'

'I like sitting on the floor. Don't you?'

'Yes. But Mrs. Hoffman doesn't like it. She says little gentlemen don't sit on floors.'

'But I'm not a little gentleman. And anyway, Mrs. Hoffman isn't around just now. So why not try it?'

Rather stiffly, he sat down, not too near to her. He would not look at her so she hugged her knees and looked away, towards the empty fireplace, and out of the tail of her eye she saw him furtively glancing at her and away again. She smiled.

'Who's Mrs. Hoffman, anyway?'

'She's the housekeeper.'

'Oh. I don't think I'd like a housekeeper.'

'She's very nice,' he said unenthusiastically, like a well-rehearsed young actor.

'Wouldn't it be wonderful if it were winter,' she said, 'and we had a big, roaring fire burning.'

'Oh, we never have a fire. Not even in the winter.'

She stared at him, wide-eyed. 'You don't? Why ever not?'

'Mrs. Hoffman says it's unnecessary. The house is always beautifully warm. We have winter air-conditioning, as well as summer.'

It occurred to her that Mrs. Hoffman was going to be a problem. And she was tempted to laugh at the solemnity of this serious-faced twelve-year-old telling her about the heating system.

She took his lead.

'It's nice and cool now. It's a very beautiful house.'

'Thank you. I'm glad you like it.'

'The grounds look very pretty. When we've had dinner, do you think you might show them to me?'

'Well, tonight it might be too late. Mrs. Hoffman likes me to be in bed by nine o'clock.'

'But this is a special occasion. I think we might persuade Mrs. Hoffman that you can sit up late.'

His dark eyes widened. 'Oh, she never lets me. Not for anything.'

'Not even when—when your father has a birthday?'

He looked puzzled. 'Oh, my father never has a birthday.'

This shattering piece of news rather disposed of that particular theory, but she stood her ground doggedly.

'Well—tonight is special. And I'm going to ask your father if you can sit up. Would you like that?'

'Yes, ma'am.'

'And please don't call me ma'am. Call me . . .' She hesitated, then abandoned dignity. 'Call me Ziggie.'

'Oh, I couldn't call you that,' he said, with evident embarrassment.

'Why not?'

'Mrs. Hoffman says little gentlemen don't call grown-ups by their first name.'

She resisted a wild temptation to say 'to hell with Mrs. Hoffman'. Instead, very guardedly, she said:

'Well, I think it will be all right this time. Because I've asked you to. And I'm sure Mrs. Hoffman tells you that it's polite to do what you're asked if you possibly can.'

'Yes,' he said uncertainly.

Further crisis was averted at that moment by Paul's entrance. She did not hear him come in, and started when his voice said softly:

'This looks very cosy. Am I intruding?'

'Paul. . . .' She laughed. 'Come and try out the rug.'

He crossed the room, and stood looking down at her.

'Fool that I am, I've always thought rugs were things you stood upon.'

'But they can be magic carpets.'

Laughing, he swung down between them. He had changed into a smoking jacket, and she thought proudly: Oh, he looks so good when he laughs, so rested . . . young.

Very solemnly, she said:

'You know something?'

'What?'

'I'd just adore to have Mrs. Hoffman come in right now.'

'She'd think we were out of our minds.'

'Paul.'

'Yes?'

'Who is this paragon?'

'A very excellent housekeeper.'

'You know, sight unseen, I wouldn't be surprised if she didn't have to go.'

'Why?'

'She likes little gentlemen. I like little boys.'

He glanced across at Laurie, who was watching them discreetly while trying to appear not to do so.

'Did you and Ziggie get to know each other?'

'Yes, sir.'

'Do you think you're going to be friends?'

Laurie swallowed hard. He was obviously terrified at being addressed by his father.

'Yes, sir,' he said, almost inaudibly. Then, as he looked

[193]

across at Ziggie and she smiled at him, he said in a rush: 'She's very pretty.'

Vandenberg raised an eyebrow. It was the first time he had ever heard his son express an opinion on anyone.

'Yes, Laurie. I think she is too. And she's staying with us for the weekend.'

For a moment the boy did not speak. Then he asked nervously:

'May I show her the grounds? After dinner?'

'Certainly. I'd like you to.'

'Thank you, sir.'

The musical stroke of a gong sounded, distantly, and Vandenberg got to his feet.

'That's dinner. Come along, both of you.'

He extended a hand to each, and pulled them to their feet. His son's pale cheeks had a slight tinge of colour in them, and he noted the excitement in the boy's eyes. For once he did not take his hand away when he felt the young shoulder beneath it tremble. Instead, they walked into the dining-room like that, Vandenberg with his hand on his son's shoulder. And Ziggie, ahead of them, seemed to belong by rights to this little ceremony. It was as though she had always been there. It was also natural for her to take her place at the table with all the assurance of a hostess, glance at the settings and say to him with a wrinkled nose:

'Milk. . . . For Laurie? No, that's ridiculous with dinner.'

'But milk is good for him.'

'He can have it for supper or lunch or any other time. It's very bad for him with meat. Ruins his appetite for proper food. Besides, this is a special evening. I think he should join us in a glass of wine.'

It had never occurred to him to give a child wine. He looked at her in astonishment.

'Wine. . . . Ziggie, he's twelve.'

'My dear Paul, when I was six I was allowed to join my parents in half a glass of wine on special occasions. By the time I was twelve I had graduated to a full glass. And I always ate the same food they ate.'

He was disconcerted. 'That's a European habit.'

[194]

'Possibly. My grandmother ruled us all. But we all grew up healthy and we're none of us alcoholics.'

He began to laugh. He suppressed his mirth hastily, seeing Laurie looking from one to the other of them in wide-eyed surprise. He gestured to the butler.

'Take away the milk, please. And bring Master Laurie a glass. He will have wine with us.'

Laurie looked even more terrified than usual as he stared with fascination at the pale gold liquid. Ziggie smiled at him encouragingly.

'When you drink it, take only a very little sip. And hold it on your tongue to see if you like it. You may not at first.'

Tentatively, Laurie did as he was bidden. Under Ziggie's glance the colour returned to his cheeks. He took another sip.

'It's funny,' he said manfully, trying to hide a small grimace, 'but I like it.'

She has won him, Vandenberg thought. If it were bitter as gall, he would say he liked it. Because she wants him to.

Contentment filled him. He had never felt so happy. This was even more than the pleasure of being alone with her. He could look from one to the other of them, and see something growing.

'Sigrid,' he said softly, raising his glass, 'to you.'

XX

THE weekend was the happiest that Ziggie had ever known. It sped by too swiftly, an enchanted interlude that made her want to stop time and hold back for ever a future that could never be as magical as this.

After dinner Laurie was allowed to sit up, and Ziggie and the boy listened while his father played the big piano. His playing was like everything else that he did, sure and accomplished. She knew that he had trained as a very young man to be a concert pianist.

'Paul,' she asked, 'why did you give up the piano?'

'I wasn't good enough.'

'How do you know? You must have been too young then to be fully developed.'

'I was competent. My music teachers told me I would probably get by but I would never be—outstanding.'

'They can't know. Not so soon.'

'Oh yes. And I knew. Then—there was something else. I got married.' He looked across at her. 'Did I tell you about that?'

'No.'

'I will. It wasn't very edifying. It was years before I even played for my own pleasure, after that.'

'But you play often now.'

'Oh, yes. It relaxes me. I've got over the frustration of not being good enough.'

He wondered: Could I have said that truthfully—a week ago? It's strange, an audience, even of one, makes so much difference. Particularly of one, perhaps I should have said.

He played gently. It was not the way he customarily played. Usually he played when he was lonely or savage. Music, throughout the adult years of his life, had been the release that perhaps drink was to some.

Maybe if I could have taken up heavy drinking I should

ave abandoned this, he thought. By such quirks of coincidence
lo we stay civilized.

'I used to feel myself an abysmal failure,' he told her lightly.
The things I wanted to do, you see, were always the things I
couldn't do. Making money never meant much to me—I
knew I should inherit plenty. And there was no pride in
making it because my father made fistfuls, and I never liked
him. So music was going to be the thing that set me apart
from him. I suppose it was a rebellion. And he humoured me
and paid for my tuition and told me I would never be any
good. And he was right.'

I wonder, she thought. I wonder if he didn't just do to you
what you might do to Laurie—for different reasons. You
can destroy a child so easily. Such small, quick words wound
them—and mark them.

She looked across at the boy. He was not looking scared
now. His face was interested.

'You like it?'

'Yes.' There was still the shyness there. 'I—don't often
hear my father play.'

It would take so little to make them what a father and son
should be, she thought. In his own frightened way, Laurie
probably worships his father. That's why he looks so unhappy
and does everything all wrong. It matters too much. Well,
we have to make it matter less. We have to make him see that
his father is, after all, only a man.

'What were the other things?' she asked lazily.

'Ummmm?' Paul had forgotten what they were saying.

'The other things you wanted to do.'

'Oh.... Swim well. And ride a horse well. I suppose I
wanted to do everything well. And the—athletic things—I
just wasn't any good at them.'

'You seem to have done them all.'

'Yes. I made myself. But to this day I'm a poor swimmer.
And I still can't get on a horse without being terrified of
it.'

She had seen his picture in the social columns that were
among the clippings in the morgue file on him. As a younger
man he had ridden often. She remembered in particular a

picture of him with his second wife, and the story of her death as the result of a fall.

'Did your second wife ride—because you wanted it?'

'No. She lived for riding. She'd been born and brought up on a Kentucky farm; she was completely fearless. Ironic wasn't it—that she should be thrown? And I—I've always expected to be thrown, but actually I never have. I've given it up now, of course.'

'Why? Would it be bad for you?'

'Probably. But it wasn't that. Somewhere along the line I grew up. At least to that extent. I realized that I had my share of courage and I needn't go on risking my neck and a horse's just to prove it.'

She was glad that he was so easy to talk to. She had thought at first that it would be difficult to get him to talk about his past life. His former moodiness had made her feel that there would be private places where she could not tread.

Now, it was as though he had thrown all the doors open. Come inside and look, he said. You won't find much of interest here, but it's all yours to see. I have no secrets.

But there were questions she would never ask him. Perhaps because of his candour, she was not curious about his past life. She had been at first. It had been part of the legend that had been his. Now she had gone beyond that, to the man himself.

In a mood of sudden introspection, she thought: I used to be in love with the idea of a big romance, of a husband with a position in life, and money. That was what first attracted me to him. Now—it's over. If he were to crash suddenly, to come to me and say: I'm broke, we have to start all over—it wouldn't matter. It would make no difference. Without a cent, he would still be the man I want. Maybe I've grown up, too.

When they retired that night to their separate rooms, she felt that they had known each other for years and had been approaching this point inevitably. She tucked Laurie in and kissed him good night, inwardly wondering whether he would let her. But he did not seem to mind her show of affection. Paul too stood beside her and bade his son good night. It bothered her a little that he did not kiss the boy, but she supposed men were like that. Yet her father had always kissed er brothers, as well as herself. Well, in time, she thought. Maybe I'm just a sentimentalist. I think children are made to be loved.

For a while she lay awake in the wide, luxurious bed in the blue guest-room. It was a beautiful room—with enough austerity to belong in a country house. The whole place had an individual touch. It was not the work of decorators or of a woman. She guessed that Paul had amused himself with it as with a new toy, before he had lost interest. She liked the cool wedgewood charm of the blue and white around her, and the severely striped chintz. On the dressing-table was one huge silver bowl, full of pink roses. She guessed they had been gathered especially for her, and she wondered by whom: the unseen Mrs. Hoffman? Dreamily, she slipped off into sleep. The rustlings of the trees outside were the only sound to disturb the complete silence. And as she surrendered herself to dreams, it was with the perfume of pine trees and roses in her nostrils.

Saturday they spent most of the day in the grounds. Laurie proudly showed her all his favourite places, of which the first was Hunter's Run itself and an exciting, fairybook twist of the brook where two trees leaned over it. In the fork of their branches he had rigged up a secret house for himself, a little platform above the gurgling water where he could lie unseen and watch the little animals or read his books. He was a great reader, she discovered. As she had guessed, he knew every inch of the huge estate, and she wondered how many solitary hours he spent roaming the soft green slopes.

She noticed that the child was most carefree and natural when she was alone with him. When Paul joined them restraint came back to him and tied his tongue, and Paul himself seemed powerless to overcome it. He didn't know how to talk to children. It struck her as odd that one who could be so understanding and gentle with adults should be so awkward with his own child.

By tacit understanding, it seemed, they both knew that this weekend was to be a family affair. They had no meals alone together. Ziggie did not regret it. There would be plenty of time for being alone, once they were married. Now they seemed to be progressing backwards. They had skipped the preliminaries in their meeting; now they were retracing and enjoying the strangeness of first encounters, without the tantalizing wonder: Whither is it leading? They knew, and they were both content.

But, inevitably, it ended. She had told Paul that she wanted to go back by train Sunday night, and so after dinner she said good-bye to them both at the station. Laurie's face was wistful and secret again, and he shook her hand gravely and said:

'Please, come again soon.'

'I will,' she promised. 'Very soon.'

To Paul she said simply: 'It has been . . . wonderful.'

'The house will be emptier than ever,' he answered.

'Then remember—it will for Laurie, too,' she told him.

For a long moment he looked into her face, then, careless of whether anyone was watching, he took hold of her shoulder and kissed her gently.

'We'll both look for you to come back—soon.'

Then she climbed into the fussy little train, and settled herself by the window where she could see them, and waved gaily. As the train pulled out, her last glimpse of them was of Paul standing with one hand on his son's shoulder, the other upraised, waving to her.

She leant back, her eyes closed. God was good. I thank you, she thought. I do indeed thank you.

XXI

ZIGGIE was completing her weekly report of allergy cases when Francesca Albertson called her.

'Oh, Ziggie, hello. Miss Albertson. Will you come into my office for a moment, please?'

The voice was silky and spiteful, as usual. Wondering, since she had little to do with Albertson, Ziggie pressed the buzzer and waited for Sarnoff to pick up his 'phone.

'Albertson wants me. Won't be long.'

'Okay, doll. Leave my door open, so I can hear the telephones.'

Sam was inside.

Ziggie walked through the crowded general office, where the small fry of the executives and their secretaries were housed. This was not lushly carpeted and exotically decorated like the front offices. It was one of Fran Albertson's grievances that she had her office opening off the main room, rather than up front. She had always felt herself entitled to a front office, which she had had in the early days of her career. But rumour had it that she had fallen foul of Louis Vermeyer's then current favourite, and been demoted. Of such delicate strands were success and failure woven in The House of Vermeyer.

On the threshold of Fran Albertson's room, Ziggie paused, disconcerted. Paul was sitting beside the littered desk, legs sprawled, arms resting on the polished walnut top. Six little glass bottles stood before him.

'Hello, dear. Come in. Shut the door.'

Albertson's voice had the honey and vinegar well mixed. The honey, no doubt, was for Vandenberg. She was always, as Ziggie would have put it, all over him.

Paul looked up at her. The preoccupation of his manner lifted for a moment, and he smiled.

'Hello, Ziggie.'

'Good morning, sir.'

Fran Albertson lifted her head at his use of her first name, lik
a dog scenting fire. For a moment she looked from one to th
other, then the mask of affability once against descended upo
her face.

'Ziggie, this is a very important test. And Mr. Vandenber
asked for you and three other girls personally.'

Her smile was meant to be patronizing. Ziggie waited.

'Now. What are your favourite perfumes?'

Ziggie considered. 'Arpège. Bellodgia. And Narcisse Noi
I think.'

'Uh-hmmm.' Fran Albertson went to a closet and cam
back with a rack of eight phials. 'Smell each one. See if yo
can pick out your favourites.'

Mechanically, Ziggie went through the ritual. She identifie
the three. Albertson looked at the code numbers on the bottle
checked them against a list she held in her hand, and nodded t
Vandenberg.

'You're a smart girl, Ziggie.' To Vandenberg: 'She ha
them all correct.'

He nodded, as though expecting it. He was looking, not a
Ziggie, but at the bottles on the desk.

'Ziggie. We're going into the perfume business. You ma
know that there isn't a trickier business in the country. W
don't want to make mistakes.' He paused, and she waite
silently, disturbed. He went on: 'We've done some preliminar
work already. Now, I want you to smell each of these si
bottles. Tell me which you like.'

Something new, she thought. It cut across the unspoke
wish that she had harboured. Could this man retire? Wh
did he want to get into the perfume business? Sure, she kne
what a rat-race it was.

She lifted each bottle in turn and put it to her nostrils. H
watched her. As she put down the last bottle, she hesitated
Then she said abruptly: 'None of them.'

'Why?'

'They smell—ordinary. I wouldn't switch to any of them.
He smiled faintly. Fran Albertson seemed annoyed.

'Ummm . . . Now, let me ask you another thing. Th
perfumes you named as your favourites are pretty expensive

[202]

We're not aiming for that market yet. What about some cheaper fragrances?'

Without hesitation she named five more, all domestic. He nodded approvingly, then turned to Albertson.

'She knows her fragrances, Miss Albertson. I'd like you to work closely with her on this. Have her go with you to the plant. Tell Stanbrook she's your special consultant on this project. Better, I'll tell him.'

'Of course, Mr. Vandenberg. If you think it's necessary. . . .'

'I do. She's more typical of the consumer than any of the rest of us. You and I are too close to the business.'

His smile was both knowledgeable and kind. It was his way of telling her he didn't trust her judgment, and they both knew it.

'Mr. Vandenberg. . . .'

'Yes, Ziggie?'

'Mr. Sarnoff won't like my spending time at the plant.'

'Let me worry about Mr. Sarnoff.'

'Yes, sir.'

He stood up. 'I'll come back with you. He's in this morning?'

'Yes, he's in his office now.'

'Good.' He made a vague gesture in the direction of Fran Albertson. 'Thanks, Miss Albertson. Let me know how you get on with it.'

Away from the big clattering office and halfway down the corridor that led to Sarnoff's department, he paused, facing her. There was no one in sight.

'Something is bothering you,' he said, watching her face. 'What is it?'

She gestured vaguely with her hands. She did not quite know herself. But she felt hurt, almost angry.

'A new line. Why? Why do you want to start up in the perfume business?'

'It's not new. I've been toying with it for some months. Just haven't had the time to give to it.'

'That's what I mean. You *don't* have the time. And you don't need it.'

He ran a finger playfully down her nose.

[203]

'Ziggie. I promise you, it won't take time away from us. I won't let it.'

'You never could give this up—could you? Just to be a human being?'

'I don't see any need to give it up—completely. But I've told you—we shall have time together. More and more time. You shall be my jailer.'

He said it very humorously, but there was no answering amusement in her face. She did not know why it troubled her so much. But she felt all at once how secondary a woman was to him. And she had thought to make him retire.

He went on: 'Do you think you could get away for lunch and a rather important piece of business? There are certain details we have to attend to, you know.'

She smiled, the shadows lifting from her face.

'I think—I could.'

'And would Saturday suit you?'

'You mean—for the wedding?'

'What else? I think we can get a special licence.'

'Yes, Paul.' The words were spoken so low he could scarcely hear them.

'Ziggie.'

'Yes?'

'You can't know—how much I would like to kiss you, just now.'

She looked away. 'I thought—you were only interested in business.'

'No. That goes on, of course. But it's not so important as it used to be. Perhaps—you *will* make me give it up. Who knows? Let's go and see Harry Sarnoff.'

He turned, leading the way, and some detached portion of her mind saw him and saw herself following him, the very distinguished President of a very successful company, and a completely insignificant junior member of the staff.

And she thought: I love him so much. So much more than he even knows. And because of the part of him that she could not possess, because there was a part of him that belonged to something else, a deep, unbearable loneliness entered into her.

Sam was sitting at his desk as she entered the room, and she saw his eyes widen as Vandenberg went through to Sarnoff's office and closed the door behind him.

'A visit from the all-high.' Since he knew that P. V. had not been behind his hiring, Sam no longer showed the same respect and admiration for him 'What cooks, Ziggie?'

She glanced at him off-handedly. 'We're going into the perfume business.'

He whistled. 'Watch that guy. You can't stop him.' Reluctantly, the respect crept back.

It was an effort to talk to Sam. She wondered what Paul might be saying to Sarnoff. Would he tell him about their forthcoming marriage? Probably not. Although they had not discussed it, she felt that he wanted no announcement until it was accomplished. And although there was no reason for secrecy, she too wished to keep it as something between the two of them. She did not relish telling Sarnoff.

Vandenberg was inside for a long time. When he left he made an appropriate comment to Sam, threw a non-committal smile at Ziggie, and that was all. And when she went in to Sarnoff to take dictation, there was no indication whether he knew or not. He simply looked at her in his normal and (as she suddenly realized) completely inscrutable way as he said:

'By the way, kid, understand you're working on the new project with the boss.'

'Yes. He wants me in on the testing.'

'Okay with me. Pretty important subject. Could be a big thing for us.'

'Yes, I imagine so.'

'Take whatever time you need after lunch. And any other time you want. Just tell me.'

'Thank you.'

It was all very easy and businesslike. The perfume tests made it seem quite normal. She was glad.

But when she had gone to lunch, Sarnoff sat for a long time staring at the wall ahead of him, his eyes narrowed to mere slits. Finally he rang for Sam.

Sam came in, and Sarnoff indicated the chair.

'Siddown. Shut the door.'

Sam knew well that bleak expression on Sarnoff's face. H
was mad. He was really mad. Sam wondered what ha
happened.

'Sam, I don't want this to go any further. But I want yo
to know.'

'Sure, boss.' The habit of subservience, unaccustomed thoug
it had been before coming to Vermeyers, now sat naturally o
Sam Woodstock's shoulders. He waited.

'Know what Vandenberg was in here for?'

'The new perfume business?' he hazarded.

'No. Oh, sure, I know about that. He mentioned it. No
Guess again.'

Sarnoff loved to play cat and mouse. It gave him a tremendous sense of power to know something that others didn'
know. But the paradox was that to prove that power he ha
to share his knowledge.

'I can't, boss.'

'Ziggie and Vandenberg are getting married.'

There was complete silence in the room. Sam stared in-
credulously.

Ziggie and Vandenberg. Never in his wildest dreams. . . .
Then he remembered. The night she insisted on taking th
package to him herself. Sure, she didn't have to. So that wa
it. Well, I'll be a sonofagun. Ziggie and Vandenberg.

'Well, how do you like that. . . .'

He could say nothing more. So, no wonder he lost out. No
that he ever stood a chance. So she got her Prince Charming
with a million dollars. With sixty million, in fact.

'Yeah. They're getting married. They're seeing to th
licence now. My little Ziggie. The two-faced, double-dealing,
lying broad. She sat there like there was nothing up, and didn'
say no word. I didn't tell her he'd told me. I know Vandenberg. I knew he wouldn't of told her he was going to tell me.
So I waited. To see if she would tell me for herself. And sh
didn't. She just sat there and two-timed me. What do you
think of that, Sam?'

'She certainly could have told us.' Sam began to fee
righteously hurt, not only on Sarnoff's but also on his own
behalf. 'That's the least she could have done.'

[206]

'Yeah. She could have told *me*. After all I've done for her. She just sat there. Didn't say a word. Looked me straight in the eye and didn't say a word. Sam, you know what this means. I can't trust her no more. Mind you, I've always had my doubts about Ziggie. I've known for a long time she wasn't sincere. But I never thought she'd do this to me. Sneaking off behind my back—and with the boss. I don't even know what she might have told him. There's no knowing what a girl will do when she's in love with a guy. And this means she's been with him. It would have to. Vandenberg ain't no boy.'

'There's nothing she could tell that would hurt you, boss.'

Sarnoff's eyes were veiled. He looked down, nonchalantly.

'No. That's right. But you never know—people tell such lies.'

Sam, what you don't know, he thought. Oh, Sam, are you a simpleton. Sure, if it was you that had been sleeping with the boss I wouldn't worry.

That lying, two-faced bitch.

Like wildfire the news spread. No one knew who started it. It may have been Fran Albertson. It may have been that someone had seen P. V. and Ziggie talking together or lunching together. It may have been Sarnoff or Sam. It spread.

Like most well-kept secrets in The House of Vermeyer, it took just two hours to reach the ladies' room. And like all such secrets, by the time it had completed the circuit, it bore little resemblance to the truth. But it was now gospel. No one disbelieved it.

Ziggie and P. V. were that way about each other. They were meeting secretly. She had been seen leaving his apartment. One little detail never circulated. There was no word of their plans for marriage.

Someone remedied that. Someone ventured: Wonder if they'll get married. Maybe it's serious. No, don't be silly. Don't you know? He's married already. No. Yes, I tell you he is. It was in a magazine article. I thought he was divorced. No, he never got free. Not the last time. Why do you think he stayed unmarried all this time if he wasn't married already? Well, I never thought of that. Sure, that would explain it.

Gloria Vernon was in the ladies' room when it broke. At first there was the normal babble of feminine voices, the usual, incessant, aimless discussion of make-up. I can't do a thing with my face. Liquid Velvet doesn't seem to suit it. Miss Vernon, do you think Liquid Velvet suits it? Or should I try Caress of Youth? I get so many blackheads. 'Course, I just *love* our products. The new shade's divine, just divine. But . . . my skin is such a *mess.* . . .

And I told her, straight out, I wasn't testing. I'm sick of testing. Every time my boy comes up I'm on test and I have to wear the wrong colours. Why should I test all the time? They don't pay me for it. Let someone else do it.

My dear, I tell you it's the best shampoo I've used. I got Albertson to give me a sample. You get one. It's wonderful, absolutely wonderful. . . .

Gloria Vernon was shutting it all out. She smiled graciously when she was addressed and made appropriate answers, but she was shutting her mind to it. And then she realized that the tone had changed. It was quiet in the ladies' room. The steady symphony of voices, one against the other, had levelled out, and Marie Hetherington was saying:

'I tell you it's all over the place. Everyone's talking. Ziggie was seen leaving his place.'

'Ziggie Anderson. . . . That stuck-up little so-and-so. She was always too good for anyone. Well, what do you know. . . .'

Gloria Vernon froze. She stood for a second with her lip-stick poised, listening. Yes, they were talking about Vandenberg. Ziggie and Vandenberg.

She put her make-up away with a hand that was shaking violently, and this time it wasn't because of a hangover. She hadn't had a drink since her interview with Pollovic last week.

Slowly, with a mechanical smile on her face, she edged away from them and out of the door. She returned to her own office. There was no class in progress, and the room was deserted. She sank down on her chair behind the desk up front with the blackboard behind her. It was like a regular school-room, and there had been a time when it thrilled her ridiculously to see that blackboard, and the pretty little pink desks that were not desks at all but make-up chests with tops that lifted up and became mirrors. Yes, her school had been fun at first.

But she was not thinking of that now. She was thinking of those voices in the ladies' room.

So it was all over the place. Everyone was talking. Everyone knew about Ziggie and Vandenberg. And he would think she had spread it. Oh, Mother of God, it wasn't fair. She hadn't said a word. She hadn't breathed one word of it, not even to Harry.

But he would think she had. He would look at her with those disillusioned eyes, and say: So you had to talk. Even though I was generous to you, you had to talk.

And now it was over. There wouldn't be any time to look around, to get herself back on her feet. She would have to leave at once. She couldn't blame him.

Why didn't I save my money when it was coming fast? I don't have any savings. I'm not even in the clear. I owe for my beaver coat and I have two charge account bills unpaid. Not to mention the liquor bill. And I haven't the slightest idea where I'll find another job. Who wants a jughead?

She wondered how long it would take for the rumours to get back to the President's office. Not long. Shaw would hear it. Shaw who had come to the company with him. He would know about it before the afternoon was out.

And then she lost her head. She got up, put on her perky little straw hat, seized her handbag and gloves, and fled.

XXII

I**T** was late when Ziggie returned to the office. She was walking on air. Lunch had been wonderful, their plans were started, and tonight she would be seeing Paul again.

He had been invited to attend a charity affair, a Polish Ball. Normally he would have sent a cheque and his excuses, but it had occurred to him: Ziggie might like it. So instead he had accepted.

She had been delighted when he told her.

'Paul—what fun. Long dress?'

'Yes, child. Long dress.' And very soberly, he added: 'There haven't been many long-dress occasions, have there?'

'It doesn't matter. There will be.'

'Yes. There will be.'

And not for the first time, he thought: What a courtship. And for a girl with her background. With parents who live by the country club book, I'll wager. Well. She wouldn't be for me if it were important to her.

So he was going to pick her up at her apartment, and Sharon would be able to meet him, and that too made it even more memorable. Now she could tell Sharon the whole story.

Sarnoff was in a quiet mood when she returned. She knew now from Paul that he had been told of their plans. She greeted him almost shyly.

'Mr. Vandenberg told me he had spoken to you—about us,' she said diffidently.

'Yes, honey. I wish ya lots of luck.'

'Thank you.'

'I hope you know what you're doing,' he went on, still in the same quiet voice.

It was like a douche of cold water on the head. She saw the narrowed eyes, the thin line of the mouth. She was wary.

'I love him, Mr. Sarnoff.'

Sarnoff picked his teeth eloquently with a paper clip. He spat the one word at her:

'Horseshit.'

Cheeks flaming, she went out of his room. For a moment she sat at her desk, saying nothing. Sam was busy with some papers and didn't look up. His absorption was so obvious that she remembered. The door was open. So he knows, too.

She had known that Sarnoff would take it hard. He would take it as an act of personal disloyalty. It was unreasonable, but that was the way he was. Well. To hell with him. She didn't have to take it.

Methodically, she packed up her desk.

Sarnoff came and stood in the doorway, and watched her. 'What do you think you're doing?'

'Going home.'

'It ain't five-thirty yet.'

'I'm aware of the time.'

'I have work for you to do. What you think this is—a debootants get-together?'

'I don't like your language, Mr. Sarnoff. Any time you want to give me some work you can keep your mouth clean.' She pulled on her gloves and picked up her straw bag. 'Good night, Sam.'

And without another glance at Sarnoff she was gone.

Sam looked up, and Sarnoff grinned at him. Sam didn't understand the grin and he didn't know what to say. He thought it best to smile back, even though he didn't see what was so funny.

'The little bitch. Just because she's hooked the big boss.'

Sarnoff's grin widened. He saw the uncertainty in Sam's face, because he knew him like a book. No, Sam, he thought, not because of that. Because she's Ziggie. She ain't changed. She never would take nothing. Only you wouldn't know about that. Because you ain't smart. And you ain't Ziggie. You've fallen into line.

'Yeah,' he said. 'Just because she's hooked the big boss.'

Then he looked about him. There were a few files on the cabinets and some papers on Sam's desk. Sarnoff's own desk was littered.

He had to find something wrong. He had to assert himself. He was mad at Ziggie, but she wasn't there, so Sam would do. He spoke to him brusquely:

'Come on, Sam. Clean up the office. Get my desk clear. Jesus, this place looks like a crap game. I want this office tidy, you hear? Because Ziggie ain't going to be around here much longer I ain't going to have the place looking like a crap game. Until she's replaced, this is your job, understand?'

Sharon was in the bath when Ziggie arrived home. She hammered on the door, impatiently.

'Sharon—hurry out of there. I have to get in.'

She flew to the bedroom and began bringing out clothes. Sharon emerged, towelling her damp red hair.

'What's the big rush?'

'I have to dress. Formal.'

Sharon paused. 'With Paul?'

'Yes.'

'What's the occasion?'

'Some big affair. Something he's honorary something of.'

'And he's condescending to take you with him?'

Ziggie stood quickly upright. 'Sharon. That isn't fair.'

'Perhaps not. But perhaps I don't think he's fair. This is as good a time as any other to talk about it.'

Ziggie looked at her wryly. Oh dear. Where do I begin? She hadn't seen Sharon since last Thursday morning. And the world had changed since Thursday.

'Sharon. Hold your horses. I have news for you.'

Sharon stopped towelling. Something in Ziggie's face told her the news. Slowly, astonishment spread over her countenance.

'Ziggie. . . . Don't tell me he's asked you to marry him.'

'Yes, Sharon. I couldn't tell you because it all happened so quickly. And he wanted me to go down to his country place to meet his boy over the weekend. Oh, Sharon, I can't begin to tell you. He's so . . . out of this world. He's not what you think. He's kind, understanding. And he's unhappy, too. He has the most adorable twelve-year-old son, and he wants us to get along. . . . Sharon, Sharon, I love him so much.'

Sharon still stood and looked at her. It was as though she didn't believe it, even now.

'Sharon—aren't you going to wish me happiness?'

There was something forlorn in that. Sharon smiled, ruefully.

'Ziggie, my dear, I wish you all the happiness in the world.'

But there was not the right ring to it. Ziggie remembered Sarnoff's 'I hope you know what you're doing'. And she felt hurt. All right, she hadn't expected any wild rejoicing from Sarnoff. But Sharon—she had thought Sharon would be glad.

She took her bath and began to dress. Sharon came in and watched her.

'Ziggie. I'm sorry.'

'About what?'

'I hurt you. By not being enthusiastic. It's only—that he isn't the sort of man I thought you'd marry.'

'You haven't met him.'

'No. But he's been married three times already.'

'He wasn't happy before.'

'And you think he will be, with you.'

'I *know* he will be. I can *make* him happy.'

'Then that's all that matters, my dear.' Sharon smiled wistfully. 'May I get to meet him, some day?'

Ziggie nodded, tremulously. She didn't know whether to laugh or cry.

'Tonight.'

'Tonight?'

'He's coming here. To pick me up. I wanted—I wanted you to meet him. Oh, Sharon, you *will* like him, you couldn't help it.' She picked up a hairbrush and began brushing her hair vigorously. 'I know why you feel the way you do. We got into this thing all upside down. We haven't done anything the right way. But—don't you see. . . . Sometimes you have to. Paul isn't like the men you and I meet.'

'I know. I do see.'

She didn't, but what the hell. She was crazy about the guy, all right. And who am I to say what's best, Sharon thought bitterly? I don't see anyone taking Jerry's place.

She had cocktails waiting when the doorbell rang. She had put on her most becoming house-robe, and brushed her red hair until it gleamed. In spite of her disapproval, she was aware of a tremor of excitement as she pressed the button to admit Paul Vandenberg.

So I'm to see Ziggie's dream man, she thought sardonically.

Then she opened the door, and Vandenberg was standing there, hat in hand, smiling at her gravely.

'You must be Sharon,' he said.

She felt like a schoolgirl as she motioned him inside. He had that way of making a woman feel completely vulnerable. She wasn't prepared for the effect he produced in her. In tails he was more handsome than she had expected him to be, but more than that she was aware of the irony of his personality, of a sense of 'I have done everything and seen everything and what has it profited me?' that pervaded him. Oh yes, she thought, he is . . . fascinating. And he knows women. He knows everything about us.

Over cocktails, with a disconcerting directness he said to her:

'I suppose you disapprove of this affair?'

'Why should I?' she parried.

Most nice young women would disapprove. And it is abundantly clear that you are a—nice young woman.'

'You make it sound like a rather unpleasant disease.'

He laughed softly. He noticed that she had not answered his question.

'Did Ziggie tell you we were planning on being married Saturday?'

'Saturday. . . . She didn't tell me it would be so soon.'

'It will be a very quiet little ceremony. But I hope you will be there. I know how much you mean to Ziggie.'

'We have been—very close to each other.'

'It's good that she has someone here, with her parents so far away.'

'She hasn't told them yet.'

'No. It would have been difficult. And even now—better to wait, I think. They might want the wedding postponed until they could be here.'

'Well. Would that be so bad?'

He stared at her levelly.

'Sharon, I'm not much of a catch, except financially. And

[214]

while it may seem ridiculous to a well brought-up young woman, I don't think that carries much weight with Ziggie.'

She missed neither the irony nor the gentleness of his expression. She looked at him thoughtfully.

'No. I don't think it does either—now.'

'My problem—and I would not want you to repeat this to Ziggie. . . . My problem is that I know I have stretched my health to the breaking point. I'm not being alarmist—but I want a quiet wedding, and a quiet honeymoon. No relatives. No fuss. That way, we shall be on the right road. And I promise you I shall rest, now that there is Ziggie to think about.'

He leaned back in the armchair, closing his eyes fleetingly. Then he turned his head towards her, smiling at her with that slow, strange smile that so transformed the coldness of his face.

'Forgive me. I'm very tired.'

'Won't you have your drink?' (It was untouched on the table by his elbow.)

'No, thank you. But you go ahead, please.'

His glance took in the piano in the room.

'Does Ziggie play?'

'No. My department.'

'Will you play for me?'

She shook her head.

'Why?'

'I'm not good.'

He shrugged. 'Neither am I. That shouldn't stop your playing.'

'You play the piano?'

He was surprised that Ziggie had not told her. Well, that was good. He didn't relish the idea of being discussed.

'Yes. It's my own special retreat.'

'Will you please play for me? If you're not too tired?'

It was an ingenuous request. He laughed. After a moment's hesitation, he rose and went over to the piano.

He rippled his fingers over the keys, idly, warming up. Then he stopped, and looked at her, with a half-laugh.

'You know, this ball we're going to tonight is Polish. Perhaps I should get Ziggie in the mood.'

He whipped into a Chopin mazurka. She liked the sureness

of his playing. She also noted wryly that he was playing for Ziggie, not for her.

Then, with scarcely a pause, he went on to the twenty-fourth prelude. The tormented, bitter melody filled the room. And as he played, his expression changed. She saw there the bitterness, the emptiness.

It's a tragic face, she thought. Then she shook herself, as the music stopped. She shivered. No, it was just the music. That is—tragedy. That prelude. She wished he had not chosen that.

'I *am* Polish tonight, am I not?' The lightness was back in his voice, and he was smiling again.

'You play superbly,' she said. She felt almost angry. There was strength and passion in his fingers. She had not expected him to move her. 'There's so much in that prelude—longing, pride, bitterness. When I play it—it all comes out pat.'

She shrugged her shoulders, and walked angrily back to her chair. He was interested.

'Music means something to you.'

'Oh, yes, it means a great deal. I live for it. And when I play myself, it's no good. I strike all the right notes, and people tell me I'm very good, just as they might say "that cake's delicious". I just—haven't got it.'

'You have to learn to let go,' he said, quietly. 'Loving music isn't enough. I found that out. You have to have—some sublime, irrational force within you that can't be taught.' He was staring ahead of him, puzzled. 'I don't always play as well as I did just now. Yes, that was good. I felt it. It was different.'

She could not take her eyes from his face. Its expression changed constantly. She remembered Ziggie's words, describing him: 'out of this world'. She wondered: Does Ziggie understand even the half of him? But even as the thought occurred to her, she realized that Ziggie didn't have to: she was in love with him.

'What kind of a man are you?' she asked him, very quietly.

He laughed, and the mood broke.

'A very—tired man.'

Ziggie's voice came to them from the doorway.

'Good evening.'

She was standing with one hand on the frame, wearing a

dress that cascaded to the floor in tiers of white tulle. Her shoulders were bare, and she wore a narrow band of black velvet at her throat. Her hair was swept up on top of her head and caught there with a chaplet of pearls.

He drew a deep breath.

'I'd like—to have someone paint you, like that. Like a bride.'

She came across the room to him as he rose, and he took her gloved hands and held her off, looking at her. Then he kissed her tenderly on the forehead.

'I mustn't smear the lipstick?'

'No. You mustn't smear the lipstick.'

With a quick, impulsive gesture, she slipped her arm about him, resting her head on his shoulder.

'Sharon—what do you think of him?'

Sharon's voice was unsteady.

'I think—you've found yourself . . . quite a man.'

He reached out his free hand and caught hold of Sharon's.

'Sharon—I value that. I'm forgiven for carrying her off?'

'I think—she's a lucky girl.'

'The luck is all mine.'

Then he pressed her hand and released it, and ten minutes later, in a flurry of excitement, they were gone.

For a long while Sharon sat silently in the darkening living-room, feeling its stillness all about her as though it were a tangible substance. She had never known anything quite so empty as the room that Paul Vandenberg had just left.

XXIII

THE ballroom at the Waldorf was a kaleidoscope of pastel-shaded tulle, a whirling, shifting pattern of blue and pink and white and yellow, with here and there a touch of scarlet or a splash of purple. The dancers circled to the dizzying, intoxicating rapture of a waltz, and Ziggie, from Vandenberg's table on the very fringe of the dance floor, watched wistfully.

She had danced two of the more sedate numbers with him, but the wild polkas and lilting mazurkas were taboo. She stared at the flushed faces and sparkling eyes of the couples swirling past them, and her toe tapped eagerly to the irresistible rhythm.

He too was watching the dancers, his gaze sombre.

'I remember balls like this in my father's house. We had a huge place then out on the Island, and in the summer he gave fantastic parties. There were so many people invited I was sure he never knew them all. And then others came, without invitation. I dreaded those parties.'

'Why?'

'I was a poor dancer, for one thing. I was too shy. And I always felt—lost. It was rather like the nightmares one has as a child, when one walks round and round among strange faces, looking for someone who has—walked away. And that one face, that one beloved figure always eludes us.'

She could never picture him doing anything badly. In all his actions, now, he was so sure, so much a master of himself. She told him so.

He laughed. 'You see only what you want to see. Or perhaps what I show you.'

'You don't try to hide things.'

'I don't know. We all play a part. I rather enjoy my legend. Oh, yes, I'm quite aware of it.'

'Yes. I knew that when you asked me how it felt to be on the same couch with sixty million dollars.'

'I said that?'

'You terrified me.

'I didn't know it.'

'I too put up a show. I suppose we all do. Unless we're arrant cowards.'

'Ziggie—don't idealize me. Or I shall disappoint you.'

'I don't have to. I love you. As you are.'

He looked into her face, his eyes still brooding, out of tune with the music.

'Don't forget—I'm the man who brings you to a ball, and keeps you tied to a table, your feet tapping the floor because he's not whole enough to dance with you.'

She flushed. Her tapping foot was stilled.

'All right.' She clipped the words off short. 'I still prefer to be at your table.'

He reached out, and clasped her hand.

'That's my girl,' he said gently, then went on in a lighter tone: 'But we must find you a partner. It's a pity to waste that orchestra. No,' as she protested, 'I want to see you dance.'

He found her a partner, a short, swarthy man with the face of a brigand. He spoke English with a very marked accent, and he danced superbly. When the first polka finished, they waited on the floor and went straight into a mazurka, and then into another and another, whirling around the enchanted room until she felt her lungs would burst and her heels take wings. There was never anything like this. All was lost in motion and music.

But when she finally returned to their table, Paul was sitting watching her, moodily, the champagne bottle at his elbow half empty.

She stood for a brief second, and in that second her glance took in his whole demeanour. The laughter went out of her eyes.

She thanked the young man. He was wiping the sweat from his face, and he lingered over her hand. He tried to persuade her to dance again, but she said flashingly:

'Thank you, I think I've danced enough. I'm exhausted.'

He shrugged, bowed smilingly to them both, showing his white teeth in the dark brown skin, and went off in search of another partner. He was seemingly inexhaustible.

There was an uneasy silence between them after he had gone. Then Ziggie said, a little breathlessly:

'I have to get into practice for such dances. Our grand-mothers must have been made of sterner stuff.'

He made no answer, but picked up his half-filled glass and drained it.

It was so unlike Paul to drink more than a glass of any wine that she was afraid. She remembered that she had not seen him drinking like this since the night she had referred to earlier. The night he made her drink brandy with him.

'May I have one?' she asked. She tried to keep the fear out of her eyes, to let him see only her love for him.

Still without speaking, he leaned over, poured her a glass, and looked around for the waiter.

'Darling . . .' She put her hand to his arm. 'We don't need any more.'

'No, that's right. I can't drink, either, can I? You see, Ziggie, what a wonderful catch I am. Because of me you will neither dance nor drink. But I'll take you to all the best places.'

The bitterness cut her like a knife. She had not seen that bitterness in his face for a long time. She turned away from him, back to the dancers, so that he should not see the tears in her eyes.

At midnight she asked him to take her home, although the dancing would go on till five. She had to get away from the maddening, incessant invitation of the music. It was a call to which her whole body responded, and there was a night-marish quality about it now, as she tried to keep her foot still and yet struggled with tears.

They were quiet on the way back to her apartment, and for once it was not the quietness of communion. She sought desperately in her mind for a way of reaching him, but he was wrapped in morose silence, as though she were not there. She wished they had never gone to the ball. She should have thought of what it would mean to him, to sit and watch. Oh, why, why, why had she been so heedless.

[220]

At her door, he began to bid her a formal good night. But he seized his hand.

'Paul—come in for a while. Please.'

'It's late, Sigrid. You should get some sleep.'

'No—come in first, please.' It seemed to her supremely important that he should come in with her.

With a small shrug, he followed her inside. He stumbled as he mounted the three front steps, and she caught her breath but did not let him see. She had lost track of how many glasses of champagne he had drunk.

There was a solitary lamp burning in the living-room, and on the cocktail table before the couch was a trayful of mixed hors-d'oeuvres, a bottle of Rhine wine in an ice bucket and two glasses. Propped against the bottle was a note. It read: 'Good night. I sleep very soundly. Sharon.'

Paul picked up the note, read it, and stood for a moment, thoughtful. Then he passed it to Ziggie.

'You must have made a conquest.'

She tried to make the words light, but there was a break in her voice. He saw the unhappiness in her face, and the black mood fell away from him. His arms went round her, he kissed her hair and her ears and forehead, and she strained his body to hers, sobbing in his embrace.

'Ziggie . . . '

'We won't go—to any more balls.'

'No, Ziggie. We don't need them.'

'Paul—we don't need anything. Only this. You and I, just like this.'

They sat side by side on the couch, and ate some of the little delicacies that Sharon had prepared for them. He reached for the bottle of wine, but she put out a hand, restrainingly.

'I don't want any. I've had more than enough.'

He set it down, unopened. He stared tenderly into her eyes.

'And I never need it. When I remember to look at you.'

She rested her head on his shoulder. For a while they sat like that, without speaking. And she was thinking: I shall have to be so careful. I must never do anything again without thinking. I must never say I want to dance. Or wear a long dress. We must do only those things that won't tire him. He must

never know that there is anything, *anything* that I'm deprive
of, because of him.

And then he moved back, away from her, and tilted her chi
with his fingers so that he could see her face. It was the gestur
that he had made the first night he had kissed her. But his fac
was gentle now.

He stared at her. Her eyes were tired and her skin shinin
from the heat of the ballroom and the summer night. Ther
was no coquetry in her face, no invitation in her set mouth
And yet the desire that he had fought down when he saw he
dancing in another man's arms arose again, fiercer and stronger
He had said to himself: No more. Not till after Saturday
But now he forgot that. Ziggie. My little Sigrid. I want you
Not pretty with that dress. Not with make-up on your face
As you are, a woman, strong and tender and yielding all a
once.

I love her, he thought, wonderingly. This *is* what it mean
She could grow old, and this wouldn't die. She could be bi
with child, and I would still want her body. In every way tha
there is—spiritual and physical—I love her. This is not lik
anything that has gone before.

'Sigrid.' He spoke her name very gently. 'Please take o
that dress.'

Her eyes widened. She glanced towards the small hallwa
beyond which lay Sharon's room.

'She sleeps very soundly,' he reminded her, a trace of a smil
on his lips.

He stood up and caught her to him, and this time he did no
kiss her hair. Finally she pushed away his impatient hands an
turned her head from him.

'Not here. In my room.'

'All right. But be quick.'

She slipped from him, the rustle of her white taffeta under
skirt filling the silence of the small hours. How quiet it is, h
thought. There was a curious, tired, strung-up intensity abou
those early morning hours. When everyone else sleeps, smal
actions have large meanings. He remembered suddenly th
numberless nights when he had worked, in the early days
When working was a deep sea in which to submerge his lonely

aching self. That had been the beginning of it, more than the desire to make money or prove himself. He could have rested on his inheritance, become a playboy. But work alone was solace. Work alone exhausted his mind and brought the sweet release of sleep. So many fatigue-ridden nights. Alone in an empty office room, without the noise of a clock, so quiet he could hear even the ticking of his own wrist watch and the moving whisper of a pencil on paper. The solitude in which great coups were planned and companies created. And there had been other solitudes. When you woke up after the first sleep, with someone you scarcely knew and now loathed, some-one whose revolting presence made you more utterly alone than you had been before.

And now—this other small-hour solitude. Sitting here, listening to all the night noises of a strange apartment, waiting for Sigrid. Knowing that she exists, that she is sharing my life even while she is not with me. Knowing that I live in her and she in me. Nothing will ever be as it was before. She is what I was searching for, even in the women who were just a means of release, even though I didn't know I was searching.

He entered her room and she had switched on the small bedside lamp. He liked that. He loved to see her and it pleased him that she was unashamed and proud of their loving.

For both of them, it was different. Something more pro-found and tender had entered into it. She knew: Now he loves me as I love him. It's not too late. And then all thought was swept aside, engulfed in the tremendous splendour of ecstasy.

There was a moment when she was suspended between worlds, then thought filled her again: This was my wedding night. I wore a white dress.

And then, too swiftly, she slipped over the edge of the world, into nightmare. She heard his sharply drawn breath, felt the rigidity of his body, almost cried out as his hands clenched convulsively on her arms. Before logical thought could tell her what to do, she was thrusting herself away from him, strug-gling to free herself from his vice-like grip.

It seemed hours before she was fumbling through the pockets of his coat for the bottle of small pills he always carried. Sick and shaking, she spilled half the contents on the carpet as she forced one beneath his tongue, then in an agony of fear she went down on her hands and knees retrieving them. And over and over her mind was repeating: Dear God, no. Don't let it be the last one. Let him live. I didn't mean it about the wedding dress. We're going to be married. We're going to have a long and happy life together. Dear God, let it be, let it be.

The attack was worse than the one she had seen before. Even when it was over, he lay spent, too ill to move or open his eyes. Once she thought in horror that perhaps he had died, so still was he. She put her head against his breast to hear the beating of his heart, and could hear it, quick and irregular. And she thanked God, jumbledly, thanking and demanding and imploring at the same time.

She did not awaken Sharon. She kept watch alone, shivering and frightened, and at one point she thought: I'll never be afraid of anything else, as long as I live. Nothing could be so horrible.

When he finally slept she crept into bed beside him, holding his hand, keeping herself very still so that she might not disturb him. And an overwhelming tenderness filled her, and she cried noiselessly into the pillow. Let me have him to look after always, she prayed. Please let me look after him, and get him well.

XXIV

AT six, Paul awoke. Light was creeping into the room and Ziggie was sleeping. He saw the marks of tears upon her cheeks, and he bent over her, brushing their smoothness with his own stubbled skin.

Instantly she awoke and turned over to him, putting her hands up to his face. That way she had of being wide awake in a moment reminded him of a child. Of his own son. When Laurie was very young, before he became afraid of his father, Paul used to awaken him in the morning and talk to him, trying to enter into the curious world of a very small boy and finding it completely baffling. But in his son's eyes there had never been the trust and devotion which shone in Ziggie's.

'You're going home?' she asked, in a low voice.

'Have to. It's six.'

'How do you feel?'

'Lousy.'

'I'll come with you.'

He shook his head. 'No need. I'll go straight to bed.'

But when he stood up he felt weak and shaken, and without further words she slipped out of bed and into the bathroom. In fifteen minutes, while he sat helplessly, his head swimming, she was dressed.

She made tea, which revived him somewhat. Even in that her thoughtfulness touched him. Most people would have forgotten that he could not drink coffee. Sick though he was, he found himself picturing their future life together. There would be someone now to think of his needs, of his little foibles. It was a thought at once strange and humbling.

She called a cab, and on the way to his apartment she held him closely, his head upon her shoulder. Then she said simply:

'Paul. Please call Dr. Hammacher. And don't go out today.'

'Not till I feel better.' He pressed her hand.

'Thank you.'

Before he got out of the cab, he turned, looking into her eyes with an expression that she could not read. He put up his hand and traced the shape of her nose with his forefinger.

'Sigrid,' he said slowly. 'It's such a beautiful name.'

Then he kissed her very gently on the lips, and left her.

When he reached his apartment, he called Hammacher, and went to bed. He felt utterly exhausted, and the pain was back. This was one of the worst. He felt frightened. He who had never been frightened before when the devil's fingers thrust that red-hot fire into his chest. Then, he hadn't cared. This year, next year.... This time, next time—what did it matter?

And now it mattered. Now there was Saturday. He wondered if prayer would help, and knew it wouldn't. You couldn't pray angina out of existence. Even if you hadn't forgotten how to pray.

The irony of it added to the pain and the fear. He felt like a child again, and wanted to cry. Why did Ziggie have to happen—now? Now when he had nothing to offer her? The others had had the best of him. The casual women, the society matrons. There was nothing left. Now, when he had found what he was seeking, there was nothing left.

Dr. Hammacher advised two days in bed, and then a couple of weeks of rest somewhere—away from work and distractions, as he put it. Vandenberg smiled ironically. Away from women and alcohol was what he meant. Well, if Hammacher had known about Ziggie he would probably have approved. Marriage would ultimately have a settling effect on his patient's habits. But he could not know about Ziggie yet.

Vandenberg was anxious to be good. He took his pills with unaccustomed docility, and slept fitfully for twenty-four hours. I have to rest, he thought. Have to get well. Must be all right for Saturday.

XXV

Harry fixed himself a long drink of limeade, and sauntered out into the sunlit garden. Harry wasn't feeling so hot. He had been out the night before, and maybe he had had too many Scotches. Or maybe it had just been that dame. Selma sure was a doll. Though he wished she hadn't come into town just now. It wasn't easy to say 'no' to a girl like Selma. She was a good friend. But it sure as hell wasn't no time to be playing around.

He should have been in the office this morning. He didn't like leaving it alone now, with Ziggie this way. But he told himself: Why worry? Anything she wants to tell the boss she's told him by now. And maybe she won't talk. She's a funny kid. And anyway, what could she tell him? Harry had never done nothing that could have hurt Vermeyers. And who could P. V. count on if not on him? And P. V. would want to count on someone now. He'd want to be getting out of things a bit. Easing up. Sure, he, Harry, knew the strain it was to a guy like P. V. We ain't none of us getting any younger, he thought. And the boss sure ain't no spring chicken to be marrying a kid like Ziggie.

So Harry stretched himself out on a long chair in his backyard, sniffed the perfume of the roses that rioted beyond the lilac trees, and closed his eyes. If he was not content, and you were never content if you were Harry, he was as near to it as he would ever come. The sun was hot, the birds were singing, and he still had a trick or two up his sleeve. If P. V. started to be difficult, there was one thing he could do: he could go over to Werkmans. They'd always wanted him. They'd still want him. They knew he was one of the reasons for Vermeyers being where it was today. They knew P. V. had wanted him to stay when he let the others go, didn't they? So quit worrying. Be smart. Take it easy. So you don't end up like P. V., with sixty million and a young bride and a ticker that just ain't no good.

But the birdsong was interrupted. He heard the telephone, faintly, in the house. He shifted into a more comfortable position. He'd told them not to disturb him. Sally would take it. He was tired. He'd told Sally he wasn't feeling so well, and she would take care of it. Sally worried when he wasn't feeling so well. Maybe she was just a good girl who loved him. Maybe she just loved the things he bought her and the certainty of the cheque she got from him every month. What the hell. You can't have everything.

But the caller was insistent. The telephone rang again. Finally, Sally came to the door leading out on to the terrace where he sat. She stood, half in and half outside the room, eyeing him tentatively.

'Well? What is it, Sally, what is it? I told you I didn't want to be disturbed. I ain't feeling good.'

He was irritated with her indecision. Sally always irritated him that way. He didn't like the scared look she got on her face. Without turning round to look at her he knew she would be looking scared, her hands nervously smoothing her cotton housecoat.

'It's the office, dear. Sam says it's important.'

'Sam?' Now what the hell did that stupid punk want? 'Why Sam? Ain't Ziggie there?'

'He didn't say, dear. He just said to tell you it was important. I told him I couldn't disturb you, the first time. But he called back.'

Harry hesitated. It might be something, at that. If Ziggie weren't there. Now where in hell was that two-faced broad? Couldn't she wait till after she was married to run out on him? That wasn't fair. He'd been good to Ziggie. She owed him better than that.

He got heavily out of his chair and shambled over to the door where his wife stood. He was yawning. Oh, my, my, my head. I sure tied one on last night.

'Okay, honey, okay. I'll take it.' He spoke in a tone of irritation, not of affection. Nobody can ever take care of anything except me, he thought. Can't even stay home for a morning without someone calling me.

Sam's tone was worried. No mistake about that. He was also scared at bothering Sarnoff in his home.

'Boss, I sure hate to call you, but I had to. Are you coming in?'

'No, Sam. Guess I'll stay home today. I ain't feeling so good.'

Sam did not try to commiserate with him or even ask what was wrong. That was odd, because lately Sam had taken to buttering him up quite a bit. Harry noticed the omission.

'Boss, I'm worried. That's why I called you. It's about Gloria Vernon.'

Instantly, Harry was alert. He said guardedly:

'Yeah?'

'I ran into her last night. In a bar. She was pretty high.'

'So this is news?' The old sarcasm was in Sarnoff's voice, but for all that he was listening intently.

'Boss, not just the usual way. This was different. She was talking a lot of wild stuff. And she was alone.'

Harry began to feel hot. He remembered the last time he had seen Gloria. Gloria, alone and drunk, and talking her head off to Sam . . . But he simply said again:

'Yeah?'

'She said she'd been fired. She was taking it pretty hard. Said she couldn't get another job, she'd tried to before. She was sure taking it hard.'

'Fired . . . The kid's crazy. Vandenberg wouldn't do a thing like that.'

'Apparently he's done it. She said so. And the funny thing— she didn't seem to blame him. Said he couldn't help himself, said it was her own fault.'

Harry was thinking fast. Something here didn't add up. P. V. wouldn't fire someone like Gloria without telling him, Harry. Of that he was sure. Unless, maybe, it involved Harry. No, don't be a baby. It couldn't be that. P. V. wouldn't know. And if he did, he wasn't the guy to meddle. So long as people were discreet. So it couldn't be that. But Gloria would be mad at P. V. That didn't add up, either. Gloria hated P. V.'s guts.

[229]

'Is Gloria in this morning?'

'No, boss. And she wasn't in yesterday or the day before. Boss. . . .'

'Yeah?'

'She was talking about . . . killing herself. Of course, I suppose it was only talk. She sure was low.'

At that particular moment, a picture swam before Harry's eyes, as though it had been projected upon a screen. The day he'd been sent round to Gloria's apartment by Louis, because they'd had a fight the night before and Louis was worried, although he wouldn't say why. And there was Gloria. All dressed up in a pretty nightdress, lying flat on her back on the bed with her hands folded together. Like a picture. Pretty as a picture. Save that she was out cold.

She'd been lucky that time. There hadn't been enough pills in the bottle. But Harry had sure sweated it out getting her back on her feet. It had been a near thing. Harry moistened his lips. His mouth was dry suddenly.

'Did you—take her home?'

'No. She wouldn't let me.'

'Wouldn't let you, you jerk. What kind of a man are you? You mean you left her in the bar?'

Sam, too, was getting hot. He'd spent a bad night. Sure, he knew he should have taken her home. But he didn't want to get involved. He wasn't Gloria Vernon's keeper, was he? And hell, he was trying to help. Better if he'd kept his mouth shut.

'Boss, when that girl's loaded, she's loaded. She wasn't listening to anybody. She just sat there drinking, and talking her head off.'

Talking about the money she owed. Talking about the things she'd always wanted to do and had never done. The things she'd wanted to do for her folks and hadn't done. Sam felt bad as he thought about it. He'd felt so bad that at five o'clock in the morning he had waked up, and not been able to sleep again, and had called her and gotten no reply. He'd even been round there this morning, trying to make her answer the door. He'd done what he could. Hell, it wasn't his fault if Vandenberg had fired her. He began to feel abused.

'Sam.' Harry spoke urgently. 'That girl tried to kill herself once before. It ain't just talk. She's that kind of a girl. You get your fanny over to her place. But quick.'

'No good.' Sam was ready for this one. 'I went there. This morning, before I came to work. She wouldn't answer the doorbell.'

Harry felt the sweat trickle down the back of his neck, and it wasn't from the sun. Oh, Jesus. If Gloria's done it this time.

'Well, go back there and break down the door, if necessary. But get in there. You gotta be quick, Sam.'

This was a fine thing. He couldn't be away from the office for half a day without something happening. He was really uneasy. *Why* had Vandenberg fired her? If he had. Maybe it wasn't only that. Maybe Gloria was in more trouble. No, don't be a kid. It couldn't be.

But Harry's heart was pumping wildly, now. He didn't want to ask Sam what Gloria had been talking about.

Sam was speaking again.

'Okay, I'll get a policeman and break in, if I have to.'

'Policeman. . . .' Harry was incredulous. What was with this guy? 'You off your head, Sam? You don't take no policeman. You think we want this on every front page in the country? You don't know Vermeyers is news, maybe? Listen. You get up there and take care of it quietly, like I would. What do you think we're paid for?'

But Sam had found his sticking point. He'd done plenty for this job. He'd been nursemaid and bootlicker and errand boy to Sarnoff, but there was a limit. He wasn't going to break into Gloria Vernon's place on his own.

'Boss, I'm not breaking into that or any other apartment. I'm sorry. I'm sorry for Gloria, but I'm not doing that. If I go up there I'll do it the right way, the proper way. I'll take someone along who has the right to break in.'

The stupid sonofabitch. Harry's mouth was a mere line. The stupid, legalistic sonofabitch. This was what he got for having a lawyer around. You didn't worry about legal niceties when a kid said she was going to jump in the river. You just grabbed her by the skirt or jumped in after her.

But he recognized defeat. Sure, Sam was stubborn. He had

[231]

the stubbornness of a little mind. Harry wouldn't be able to shift him.

'Okay, okay, Sam.' Harry was already thinking of the next move. 'So don't say anything about this to anyone, you hear? Don't say nothing. Not even to Ziggie. And get off the line and let me think.'

He hung up without waiting for a reply. He was shaking as though he had a fever. He cursed himself for that night he had taken Gloria out. He'd always been so careful in the past. No one from the office. That had been his rule. That way you didn't get involved.

But he couldn't think about that now. It would take him a good hour to get to Gloria's place. And besides, he didn't want to be the one to find her. If she'd meant business. It would look queer. It wasn't his baby. He hastily corrected that figure of speech and told himself it wasn't his problem. *He* hadn't fired her.

No. Vandenberg had fired her. A fat smile slowly settled over his face. Why hadn't he thought of that before? Sure, Vandenberg was responsible. Let him straighten it out. He wouldn't want publicity any more than he, Harry, did. Gloria was his problem. Let him worry about her.

He picked up the telephone, and dialled. Miss Shaw's formal tones answered him.

'Hiya, honey.' It always made her mad that he called her honey, and he knew it. 'P. V. in?'

'No, Mr. Sarnoff. Mr. Vandenberg will not be in today.'

Sarnoff's eyebrows went up slightly. So maybe he was getting ready for the wedding. He should have asked Sam if Ziggie was in. Well, he'd spoil their preparations.

'Is he home?'

'I don't know, Mr. Sarnoff. Shall I tell him you called if I hear from him?'

'No, doll. No need. Thanks, anyway.'

He held down the receiver for a moment, and dialled the number at Vandenberg's apartment. It was Vandenberg himself who answered, after the telephone had rung a few times. He sounded tired. Sarnoff grinned, but his voice was deference itself as he spoke.

'Boss, I hate to bother you.' It did not occur to him that he was quoting Sam. 'But we got trouble.'

Vandenberg, who was in bed, pulled a pillow higher behind his head, and leant back against it. He had done a lot of sleeping in the past two days, but he still felt tired. The sedatives he had taken were hard to shake off.

'What is it, Harry?'

Harry came right to the point. 'Gloria Vernon. Did you fire her, boss?'

Vandenberg's brows knotted.

'No.'

'Well, she thinks you did.'

This was silly. He had been explicit.

'I had a talk with her. It was necessary. I told her I wanted her to look around and find something else. But she had as long as she liked in which to find something and no one was to know.'

Not even me, Harry noted. Well, she couldn't kick at that.

'That was sure generous, boss. But she don't seem to think you meant it. She was in a bar last night talking her head off. She's been on a three-day jag. She said she'd been fired and she was going to kill herself.'

A tiny hammer began to beat in Vandenberg's head.

'That's . . . insane,' he said unbelievingly. But at the same moment, some part of his mind recognized: It could be true. She's the sort of woman who might do a crazy thing like that.

'Boss.' Harry was emphatic now. Sure, he'd been silly to get worried. This was it. If Gloria had done anything, it was P. V.'s fault. 'Some people you can't do that to. Gloria's one of them. She's sick. Okay, I know she's a jughead. But that's a sickness. She's been sick a long time. She don't drink because she can't forget Louis who died a year ago. She drinks because she's sick. She needs our help boss. You can't kick her while she's down. You gotta help her.'

The urgent, insistent voice was sincere, human. Harry was playing his favourite role. He was the good, warm-hearted guy, the champion of the little people, the rough diamond with the heart of gold. It was such a convincing performance that he quite fooled himself.

[233]

For a moment, Vandenberg did not speak. Then:

'Have you called her?'

'Sure, boss. Her 'phone doesn't answer. And my assistant was up at her place this morning, but the blinds are drawn and she don't answer her doorbell.'

Harry's imagination supplied the missing details. He could see her place, see the derelict air of those blind windows.

Vandenberg's next question showed that he, too, could see those windows. He snapped out:

'Where are you?'

'I'm home, boss. That's why I called you. I wasn't feeling so good this morning, so I stayed home. Of course, if you want me to, I'll get over there right away. But it would take an hour. More than an hour, with traffic the way it is. Might be too late. . . .'

'Harry, have your man go over there, right away. He's in the office?'

'Yes, boss. I tried that.' Harry's tone was patient. 'P. V., he ain't smart. He wasn't my choice, you remember. I never thought he was smart. He wants to take a policeman over there. Now you know we don't want that. We don't want this all over the newspapers.'

And Vandenberg, too, knew that he was trapped. You smooth, subtle bastard, he thought. You lying, two-faced bastard. You won't go over to see her. Wild horses wouldn't drag you. Because you know I'm the boss, you can pass the buck to me.

Vandenberg sat up, wearily, reached for the pad and pencil that was by his telephone.

'What's her address?'

'Nine-nine East Twenty-third Street. It's an apartment over a lamp shop. Third floor.'

'And her telephone number?'

Inwardly chuckling, outwardly sober as a judge, Sarnoff gave it to him. Okay, let him call it. Let him get no answer. It's his problem.

When Sarnoff had rung off, Vandenberg did try it. He let it ring eight times before hanging up. So what did that prove? Maybe she was still in some bar. Maybe she'd gone home with somebody. A three-day jag. When you got that low there were plenty of things that could happen.

But it might be suicide.

He let his legs dangle over the side of the bed, and sat there. He sat for perhaps two full minutes on the edge of the bed, hating Gloria Vernon with a fierce, bitter, personal hatred. But it didn't do any good. He was tired, he needed to rest; this was Thursday and he had to be fit by Saturday; he couldn't afford right now to get involved in this thing. But it was no good. As Harry had said, Gloria Vernon was his responsibility. She was one of the problems that he had taken over when he took over The House of Vermeyer. She was as much a part of the balance sheet as the profits of the last year. And he had indirectly fired her.

He dressed quickly. He had been thinking, before Harry called, I feel better. I'll have Ziggie join me for dinner somewhere tonight. Just a quiet little dinner. Then I'll come home and go to bed again. He wished he had not thought of that, because it made the thought of Gloria the more repugnant to him. The two women were so different.

Ziggie had not called him, and he was grateful for her restraint. It would have irked him to have her fussing over him. Instinctively, he knew that Ziggie would never be the woman to fuss. She might die inside, but she would keep her fears to herself. And he needed that. It left him the sense of integrity which most women took from him.

Maybe Gloria had taken that sense of integrity from Louis Vermeyer. It wasn't only his money problems that had driven him to suicide. They had been licked, thanks to Vandenberg's own generosity. In a sudden, backward flash, Vandenberg saw what it might mean to be tied to a woman like Gloria.

When he stepped out of the building into Park Avenue, the noonday heat of Manhattan enveloped him like the hot breath of a furnace. It was an oppressive day, with the sky luminously grey and the glare of cloud-screened sun bouncing off the white concrete. In his air-conditioned apartment, Vandenberg had forgotten the ferocity of the New York summer. He hailed a cab. Before they had reached the address that Sarnoff had given him, his open mesh shirt and tropical suit were soaked with sweat. He felt weak again, and he promised himself: Once this is over, I'll go back to bed and rest up till Saturday. I won't call Ziggie for dinner.

As he paid off the cab, he glanced about him, appalled. Gloria—living in a place like this? There were broken bottles and scraps of dirty newspaper littering the street. A drunk lay in one doorway, insensible. The people hurrying about their business were what he classified as garment district types.

He looked up at the windows. The shades were drawn. They stared blankly on the world. And he wondered—behind those shades—what?

He entered the small, dirty vestibule, and found her name on one of the mail-boxes. He pressed the button; there was no reply. He pressed another button, and then a third, and this time the answering buzz sounded and he pushed open the front door.

Third floor, Sarnoff had said. Three-A, from the mail-box. He ascended the stairs, slowly.

On the second landing, he paused. At first, he did not know what made him stop. Then he recognized it. A faint, acrid, sour odour. Gas.

He ran up the remaining flight, hesitated at the first door and saw that it was Three-A. He pressed the bell, and began pounding on the door, without waiting. There was, of course, no reply.

He tried putting his shoulder to the door, but to no avail. There was scarcely any give in the stout, old wood. He looked about him. There was a door opposite, and he rang that bell, and knocked on the panels with his fist.

There was no reply there either, but he heard a door on the floor above open, and someone shouted down the stairs:

'Who is it? What do you want?' Steps slopped over the corridor above, and down the stairs, and a head peered down at him from midway. 'There's no one there. That apartment's empty. They're away.'

It was a woman's head, worn and slatternly. A fat, panting body followed it into view.

'Where's the janitor?' he demanded.

[236]

'There ain't no janitor. Supposed to be, of course, but you never see one. Landlady's on the first floor—One-A.' She jerked her head towards the lower floors.

'Will you please call for a doctor. Do you have something I can force this door with?'

He had gone back to Gloria's door. The woman stared at him bovinely, her eyes not even changing. She had a round, sallow face, and she was chewing gum.

'Doctor? What for?'

'Can't you smell it? Gas.'

The smell was distinct now. The woman sniffed. 'Gas? No. You're kidding.' She made no move.

'Will you please get a doctor? And you must have something—a poker or a crowbar or something.'

The woman still stared at him, not moving. Then she glanced towards the closed door.

'That one. Fancy piece. What do you know. Gas.' She came nearer to the door, sniffing tentatively. 'Sure does smell like it. Well, how do you like that.'

In sudden desperation, he pushed past her and ran down the stairs to the street level. He found One-A, and rang the bell. It seemed to him that life consisted at that moment of endless bells. He wondered if someone would answer. Eventually he heard movements inside, and the door opened.

'Yes, what is it?' A tall, thin woman peered out at him. She had her hair in pincurls above a bony, too heavily rouged face. Her expression changed as she looked at him. 'Oh. . . . What can I do for you, sir?'

'One of your tenants—I think she has tried to kill herself.' He did not stop to think how it sounded. 'Do you have a key to Three-A? And will you please call a doctor at once?'

'Oh, my God.' The thin mouth opened and remained open, foolishly. He saw the sudden fluttering of her large hands. 'Three-A. That's Miss Vernon.'

'Yes. Do you have a key?'

'Her and her men. All the time there are men here. I should have thrown her out. Oh, my God. A suicide. . . .'

'Please—the key.'

He found that he was clenching his hands. He was strung

taut with the delays. Still the woman made no move. Instead, she asked abruptly:

'Who are you?'

With difficulty he kept his voice level. 'Miss Vernon is one of my employees. Will you please give me the key and we can talk about it afterwards.'

She disappeared into the shadows of the room. He wondered why it was so dark in there at eleven o'clock in the morning. There was an unhealthy odour, a stale, airless quality, about the entire place. He felt he was suffocating.

After minutes that seemed endless she returned, holding out her hand.

'Here's the key. And I don't want any trouble over this. I don't want the police——'

'Please call a doctor.'

He snatched the key from her and ran up the stairs. When he reached Gloria's door, his breath coming in short gasps and his heart thumping, the woman from the flat above was still standing there, chewing gum.

She watched him insert the key in the lock.

'You shouldn't run up the stairs like that. Ain't good for you. These stairs are killing. Don't know how Mrs. Farber has the nerve to charge what she does with stairs like that.' As he entered the room, he could still hear her voice behind him. 'Do you think she's dead?'

The room was dark. The stench of gas tingled in his nostrils. He swiftly crossed the room and pulled up the Venetian blinds, then tried to open the window. It was old, and it stuck. He looked about him. On a table near the window was a heavy bronze ashtray. He seized it, averted his face and smashed the window. He smashed every pane, deliberately, making as big a space as possible. The hot, humid air scarcely entered. There was no breeze.

The other two windows opened easily enough, and he threw them up to their fullest extent. Then he noticed the fire escape. Someone (probably Gloria) had had the windows taken out and glass doors put in. Beyond them, he could see plants growing in long boxes. It was like a small terrace garden suspended above the squalor of Twenty-third Street. He unbolted the doors and threw them wide, then went through to what he correctly guessed to be the kitchen.

It was an old-fashioned gas stove, without a pilot. Thank God for that, he thought. He turned off the taps, all of which had been on. Then he noticed that the smell of gas was not as strong in here. He saw why. The top of the kitchen window was an inch down. Gloria must have forgotten that she always kept it open.

Then only did he go back to Gloria. He had taken one glance at her sprawled body as he entered. She was not in bed, but was lying on the rug before the elaborately screened fire-place, her head pillowed on one arm as though she were asleep. He went over and stood looking down at her. The robe she wore was open, revealing the thin bones of her chest and the hard, muscular flatness of her body. She was a big-framed woman and she had dieted like mad to keep herself slim, and in that moment she seemed emaciated.

He knelt down, listening for her heart-beat. She was still alive. She didn't look pretty. Her hair was tangled and dishevelled and her face bore the traces of make-up that sweat had almost erased. This is the Vermeyer girl, he thought. This is the woman who used to stare at you in colour from those big, romantic full-page ads. This inert body reeking of whisky.

He could not guess how much of her stupour was due to the fumes of gas and how much to alcohol. He caught hold of her and dragged her across the floor towards the fire escape. Her feet trailed and she was a dead weight in his arms. But some-how, sweating and desperate, he got her there. He didn't know what was the best thing to revive anyone who had in-haled gas, but he turned her over on to her stomach and began to give her artificial respiration, as though she were a swimmer who had gone under. He remembered from far-off days learn-ing how to do it, from a life-guard down in Florida. He began to laugh, half-hysterically, then pulled himself up short. He was almost light-headed from the sunlight, which beat down unmercifully on the fire escape. He stood up, panting, and leaned against the wall for a brief moment. Detachedly, his glance took in the petunias growing luxuriously in their little pots, the creeping morning glory and the zinnias. The floor of the fire-escape landing had been boarded. It was another part of Gloria, like the sumptuous rooms behind him which he had vaguely glimpsed. The thought crossed his mind fleetingly: What a waste. What an appalling waste.

He heard voices in the room behind him, and re-entered stumblingly. The landlady was there, and a man with a bag.

'I'm the doctor. Where is she?'

Vandenberg pointed to the fire escape. He watched as the doctor went through, then sat down heavily in one of the ornate armchairs. He looked about him. What a place. Why in God's name should anyone want to live in such a locality if they had discrimination enough to collect such things about them?

The landlady was looking at him.

'You look—beat.'

He nodded, half-smiling. 'It's hot. I ran upstairs.'

'She's a friend of yours?'

He shook his head. 'She works for me.'

The thin face almost sneered. 'I'll be glad when she's gone. You're not free to throw anyone out these days, so long as they pay their rent. But I'll be glad when she's gone. With her men always coming here and her drinking and this sort of thing. She tried it once before. Pity they didn't let her finish it.' Again the innuendo of her thin-lipped smile. 'If she's a friend of yours, I hope you'll see to it. She can get another place. There are plenty that can't afford it, but she can. She can pay a better rent. With all her men that come here.'

He did not reply. He was sitting in the deep chair, grateful for the comfort of it, his eyes closed. He just wanted to sit there and rest and not have to get up again. If only it had not been so hot. It was so hot that he could feel the sweat running down his scalp.

He heard the doctor re-enter the room and put in a call to a hospital. He did not interfere. He was glad to have the matter out of his hands. With all the doors and windows open, the smell of gas was fainter now. He didn't think there had been enough concentration to do any real damage. Perhaps she was just drunk.

He realized the doctor was talking to him.

'I beg your pardon,' he said, sitting up with a start. The doctor was looking at him curiously.

'I was saying I'd sent for an ambulance. It should be here any minute. She'll be all right.'

He felt relieved. 'No—after-effects?'

'No. She's going to have to stay in hospital for a little while —better, anyway, in case she pulls a stunt like this again. You know her pretty well, I take it?'

'She works in my company. I feel rather responsible.'

'Quite. I understand, sir. Might I—know to whom I should apply, if—anything arises?'

'Please send your bill to Mr. Harry Sarnoff, at this address. And if there is anything else—call him.'

He handed the doctor his card. He saw the quickly suppressed surprise in the man's face.

'And—Doctor. For Miss Vernon's sake, I should appreciate it if nothing of this found its way into the papers.'

'There's no reason why it should, sir. I'll see to it.'

There was enough of a gleam in the man's eyes for Vandenberg to know that he *would* see to it. And no doubt his discretion would be reflected in his bill. Well, he didn't care. That wasn't important.

For a long time after the man had left, following the two orderlies who carried Gloria down the stairs, he sat in the same position. Gloria was still unconscious, but the doctor seemed pretty sure she would be all right. And Vandenberg felt limp and exhausted. He wanted to get home, but he could not make his body move. It cried out to him to rest, rest, just for a little while.

Finally, he rose, and went slowly downstairs. He rang the landlady's bell again, and this time it was opened quickly.

'I don't know whether Miss Vernon has paid your rent up to date——' he began, but she cut in quickly.

'Oh yes. It's always paid promptly.'

'Well. She will be in hospital for a few days. I wouldn't want her bothered when she returns.' He pulled out his wallet and drew out some fifty-dollar bills. 'This should take care of—any delay that there may be. I wish it understood that she is not defaulting in her rent.'

[241]

Reluctantly, the woman took it.

'I told you, sir, and I don't mind telling you again. I'd sooner have her out of here.'

'That is something you must discuss with Miss Vernon when she is well. But I would appreciate it if you would not raise the issue until she is fit to cope with it.'

He bade her good morning, aware all the while of the satirical hardness of her face. It was a face a Toulouse Lautrec might like to paint. It had in it all the knowledge, the sordidness, the malice of the back streets of the big city in which she had spent her life.

He went quickly from her, let himself out into the noise and sunshine of the street, and looked about him for a cab. There was none in sight.

He hesitated, and as he did so he felt it: the familiar, dreaded, warning pain. He stood quite still. This was the pain his body had feared. This was why his body had refused to move from that chair. But his brain had been too tired to heed the fear.

Slowly, he walked to the corner.

Cab, he thought. Got to get a cab.

He stood on the sidewalk and raised his hand to one, but it had a passenger. As he watched for another, the stab of pain came again. It was worse, almost paralysing him. He dared not move. He just stood still, waiting, afraid, afraid even to walk.

Very cautiously, he felt in his pocket. It was empty. The bottle of pills was not there. Then he must have put it in another pocket. Frantically, yet without too much movement, he went through one pocket after another. But he knew. From that first moment when he had put his hand into his pocket and found it empty, he knew. In his mind's eye the picture of the little bottle on his night table tormented him. It had been there while he was talking to Sarnoff. He had forgotten to put it into his pocket when he left the apartment.

'Cab, sir?'

He stared unseeingly at the driver of the yellow De Soto, then staggered towards it as the man was almost about to drive off.

The man eyed him curiously. Some people sure start their drinking early....

'Where to, sir?' he asked. And repeated patiently, as Vandenberg hesitated, his hand on the door handle: 'Where to, sir?'

And then Vandenberg remembered something else. The will. He'd never changed his will. Ziggie would get nothing. It was ten minutes to his apartment, even if the lights were with them. And five more to get across the lounge and up to his room. He'd never make it. And Ziggie would get nothing.

'Telephone,' he croaked. 'Wait for me.'

'There's a telephone right behind you, sir. In the drug store.'

The sun dazzled him, and he made his way to the drug store like a blind man. There were two call boxes, and he entered one. The pains were coming fast now, like burning fingers in his chest. His hand was shaking so much he could scarcely insert the dime.

Drug store. They would have his pills. Any druggist knew what to give for angina. The pain again, the pain that drove thought and speech and even will from him. He couldn't remember his attorney's number. He couldn't even remember his name. He was suffocating, clawing at the glass wall. If he could get out.... But he couldn't get out. The weight of his body was against the folding door, wedging it shut. He could see nothing. He could not drag himself away from the door. He was trapped.

Hear, oh Israel: the Lord our God is one Lord ... God of Abraham, God of Jacob....

Darkness. Darkness and agony and suffocation. Hear me, oh God. God of my fathers, help me. Lo, though I walk through the Valley of the Shadow of Death, I shall fear no evil, for Thou art with me, Thy rod and Thy staff they comfort me....

What a way to end it all. In a telephone box. Ziggie, I love you. Ziggie....

In the small cage of glass and wood, six feet away from two teenagers laughing over their ice cream sodas, while the

[243]

juke box played 'The Young in Heart' and the first down-at-heel customers came in for early lunch and the attendant called out 'One medium rare on'—in that small, confining cage, the second President of the House of Vermeyer died.

XXVI

FRAN ALBERTSON was in a Salary Advisory Committee Meeting when the news reached her. She forgot abruptly the fine arguments she had been marshalling in order to kill a salary increase for a junior secretary she disliked. She got it over the telephone, from Huberman.

'My God, Fran. . . . Have you heard the news? Vandenberg is dead. Collapsed and died in a drug-store telephone box. I still can't believe it.'

She could not believe it, either. Not at first. Such things didn't happen to a man like Paul Vandenberg. And then the truth of it penetrated. She saw it reflected in other faces.

And she thought: My God. With so much to live for. All that money. And he's dead. Then she remembered the gossip, and wondered: Does Ziggie Anderson know?

Swiftly, the news ran. In the ladies' room the usual bedlam of shrill feminine voices was hushed. No one knew the details. They knew only that Vandenberg was dead. As suddenly and spectacularly as he had come among them, he had gone.

Miss Shaw entered in the midst of it, and they were all silent, because they saw she knew. She gave them one despairing, hostile glance, and then leaned up against the wall, sobbing. They felt embarrassed, because they knew she had been with him for fourteen years. Her usually immaculate hair was untidy, and she just stood there, her face contorted into ugly folds, her body racked by a grief so personal and so devastating that one by one they left the room, until she was alone.

The men were quiet, speculative. For many of them, after the first shock of surprise, the reaction was a selfish one: How will this affect me? The House of Vermeyer had known upheaval once before; now its new head, too, was gone.

When Sam Woodstock heard of it, he was silent for a full minute. It was unbelievable. But on the heels of the stunned surprise came other thoughts. He guessed at the result. This meant Sarnoff would take over. It would have to. Vandenberg had never appointed anyone else. Sarnoff, his boss—the new head man.

His pulse beat faster. If Sarnoff were President—maybe there would be a chance for him, after all. Maybe he had been smart to hang on and take all the crap that Sarnoff threw at him. Thoughtfully, he went back to his office. He wondered if Sarnoff knew.

He knew. He was sitting behind his big desk, his face expressionless. Sam could read nothing in it. He was just sitting there, his hand idly playing with a paper clip, his gaze on nothing in particular.

He glanced up as Sam entered.

'You heard,' Sam said quietly.

'Yeah. I heard.'

And that was all. Sam stood there, not knowing what to say.

Sarnoff picked up the paper clip, and thoughtfully picked his teeth.

'Two presidents,' he said musingly. 'Two presidents, in a year. Both dead. One under the wheels of a train, the other of a heart attack. And I may be the one to take over.' He looked up at Sam, his face grey. 'Maybe it's a jinx.'

Sam stared.

'Boss—that's no way to talk.'

Sarnoff stared at him sombrely. 'No. I ought to be glad. Because they both thought they was smarter than me, and I'm left. I'm alive. I may fill their shoes.'

He shrugged his shoulders, as though he were shrugging something off. That grey, unhealthy look in his face was still there.

Sam thought: I'll never know this man. I never know what to expect from him. What the heck. . . .

Sarnoff looked at him suddenly.

'You seen Ziggie?'

'No, sir. She went out somewhere—fifteen minutes ago.'

'Did she know?'

'No—I'm pretty sure she hadn't heard.'

[246]

'We gotta tell her, Sam.'

Sarnoff crumpled a sheet of paper suddenly in his thick, blunt-fingered fist. Sam wondered if he knew what it was he was destroying, and felt sure he didn't.

'Shit,' he said savagely. 'Of all the dirty, low-down deals. A kid like Ziggie.' He stood up, paced slowly across the room, scratching his thinning hair, and then jerked his head at Sam. 'Find her. And send her in to me.'

'Yes, sir.'

As he went out, Sam thought again: No, you just never can know this man.

And he thought too of Ziggie, and he said to himself: The poor kid. Oh, Jesus Christ, the poor kid. Why does it have to be this way?

He didn't often blaspheme, he was a good Catholic, but the enormity of this thing smote him. He remembered the way she had looked when she came back from that long lunch, Monday, all suppressed excitement and sparkle, like a dozen fireworks were going off inside her. Something had gone wrong, she'd been quiet and worried since, but that way she had when P. V. spoke to her on the 'phone. . . . Sure, she was in love with the guy. And oh, Mother of God, this didn't have to happen. It could be such a beautiful world, if someone didn't always pull the rug out from under you just when you thought you were sitting pretty.

He heard the quick tap-tap of Ziggie's high heels as she came down the corridor. One glance at her face and he knew he didn't have to break the news to her. He said quietly:

'Sarnoff wants you.'

She nodded, without speaking, picked up her notebook and pencil, and went inside. She closed the door behind her.

Sarnoff looked at her. There was no trace of feeling in her face, just a chalky whiteness of the skin and a compression about the lips. Sarnoff came around his desk, and stood in front of her.

'You don't need the notebook, kid.'

She put it down on the edge of his desk, very gently. All her movements were controlled, almost as though she were afraid she might break something.

'You heard.'

'Yes. Everyone's talking about it.' Her voice was flat.

He didn't like that flat voice and her still body. Didn't do to take things like that.

'You don't have to keep up with me, kid. You go ahead and cry.'

She looked at him, bleakly. 'I can't. Funny, isn't it? Shaw was sobbing her heart out in the ladies' room. And I can't cry.'

'Shaw's been with him a long time, kid. Guess she was pretty fond of him.'

'Yes,' she said dully.

Then she said something that made him turn away from her, so that she could not see his face. She said with sudden passion:

'What was he doing down there, anyway? Did his business mean so much to him that he couldn't leave it, even to rest for our wedding? Was it so important? What was it, Sarny? What was it? The perfume project?'

The bitterness was like a blazing fire in her white face. He felt uncomfortable. She'll find out anyway, sooner or later he thought. Sam will talk. Even if I can keep it out of the newspapers. Better tell her.

He turned back to her.

'No, kid. It wasn't the perfume project. It was Gloria Vernon. She tried to kill herself, and he went down to her place because he felt responsible. Because he was that kind of a guy.'

He saw her eyes widen. 'Gloria. . . . Why?'

He shrugged. 'She's a crazy kid. She got the idea she was through. He didn't mean it that way. He was generous. She took it wrong. And he—he felt responsible. He had to stop it.'

For a moment, she continued to stare at him. And then she said slowly:

'Gloria. . . . Is she all right?'

'Yes, kid. He found her in her apartment. She'd turned the gas on. But it wasn't enough to kill her—the hospital called me.'

'And for that—for that, he's dead, Sarny.'

There didn't seem to be any answer to that. He moved slowly across the room, standing close to her.

'You ain't called me Sarny in a long time, kid.'

He ran his hand gently over her head, with the same rough tenderness that he might show to his own daughters. The ice in her heart cracked. She closed her eyes and put her clenched fist against her mouth, and sobbed helplessly.

He let her cry, not touching her, knowing that she wanted no other arms about her now. When it was finally over, he said to her gently:

'Ziggie, maybe you'd better go away for a while.'

'I want to go away. Perhaps for good.'

'Anything you want, you only got to name it, kid. You know that.'

'Thank you, Sarny.'

'It ain't from me. It's what he'd want.'

For a moment she was silent, trying to prevent the sobs that again shook her. Then she said in a muffled voice:

'We were—going to Maine. . . .'

'Maybe you should go home, Ziggie.'

'No. Not home. Not yet. Perhaps not ever. Maybe I'll go south. What difference does it make. There are so many places.'

Yeah, he thought. So many places. And for her, they'll all be empty.

He picked up his hat.

'Come on, kid. I'll take you home. And I'll buy you a drink on the way.'

A drink would help. A drink always helped. Sometimes it was the only thing you could do for a person. Buy 'em a drink, let 'em talk. Let 'em cry, sometimes. What the hell. What could anyone do?

She let him steer her to the door. She seemed completely apathetic. They went out through the big general office, and the main showroom, and people looked at them, staring at Ziggie. But Ziggie didn't see that they were staring.

And Harry remembered Gloria when she heard about Louis. He had bought her a drink, too.

[249]

Two of them, he thought. Two smart guys. Smarter than I am. And they're gone. And there's just me, to cheer up their girls and take care of the business for them.

Me—Harry the Bum.